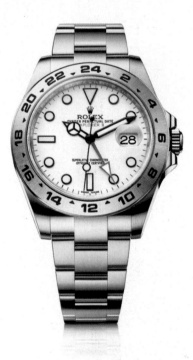

| CONTENTS

MARCH 2017 • VOL. 231 • NO. 3 • OFFICIAL JOURNAL OF THE NATIONAL GEOGRAPHIC SOCIETY

D0714558

ELSEWHERE

TELEVISION
TAKE A JOURNEY THROUGH HUMANITY'S ORIGINS

Humanity has progressed thanks to a sequence of quantum leaps, including the discovery of fire, the dawn of communication, and the first stirrings of war. National Geographic's new series *ORIGINS* delves into these and other advances Mondays at 9/8c, starting March 6.

TELEVISION
THE LANDMARK SERIES EXPLORER IS BACK

Long a popular documentary series, Explorer returns with magazine storytelling, celebrity guests, and conversation, hosted by Richard Bacon. Mondays at 10/9c on National Geographic.

STOP-MOTION VIDEO
JOIN THE VOYAGES OF A VIKING SHIPBUILDER

In a video adventure rooted in Norse mythology and fashioned entirely of handmade paper art, a Viking master builder constructs a ship, then pilots it on raids to take loot and slaves. See it at *ngm.com/Mar2017.*

360-DEGREE VIDEO
EXPERIENCE A BATTLE WITH VIKING WARRIORS

Armed with swords and axes, armor-clad reenactors at a Viking festival in Wolin, Poland, launch an offensive against the Slavs – and you can be part of it. Find our immersive 360° film at *natgeo.com/vikings360.*

TELEVISION
CESAR HITS THE ROAD...

In *Cesar Millan's Dog Nation* the dog behavior expert and his son Andre tour the United States helping owners and pets. The series debuts March 3 at 9/8c on Nat Geo WILD.

BOOKS
...AND OFFERS CANINE 'LESSONS'

In *Cesar Millan's Lessons From the Pack: Stories of the Dogs Who Changed My Life,* the Dog Whisperer shares life lessons he's learned from dogs. Available at *shopng.com* and wherever books are sold.

NAT GEO WILD YOUTUBE CHANNEL
SEE NEW WILDLIFE VIDEOS

Nat Geo WILD looks at surprising animals found in our own backyards in a new digital series, *Untamed With Filipe DeAndrade,* airing on YouTube March 14.

TELEVISION
THE BIG CATS KEEP ON COMING

Our annual Big Cat Week kicks off February 20 on Nat Geo WILD.

Subscriptions For subscriptions or changes of address, contact Customer Service at *ngmservice.com* or call 1-800-647-5463. Outside the U.S. or Canada call +1-813-979-6845. We occasionally make our subscriber names available to companies whose products or services might be of interest to you. If you prefer not to be included, you may request that your name be removed from promotion lists by calling 1-800-NGS-LINE (647-5463). To prevent your name from being available to all direct mail companies, contact: Mail Preferences Service, c/o Direct Marketing Association, P.O. Box 9008, Farmingdale, NY 11735-9008.

NATIONAL GEOGRAPHIC (ISSN 0027-9358) PUBLISHED MONTHLY BY NATIONAL GEOGRAPHIC PARTNERS, LLC, 1145 17TH ST. NW, WASHINGTON, DC 20036. ONE YEAR MEMBERSHIP: $39.00 U.S. DELIVERY, $44.00 TO CANADA, $51.00 TO INTERNATIONAL ADDRESSES. SINGLE ISSUE: $7.00 U.S. DELIVERY, $10.00 CANADA, $15.00 INTERNATIONAL. (ALL PRICES IN U.S. FUNDS; INCLUDES SHIPPING AND HANDLING.) PERIODICALS POSTAGE PAID AT WASHINGTON, DC, AND ADDITIONAL MAILING OFFICES. POSTMASTER: SEND ADDRESS CHANGES TO NATIONAL GEOGRAPHIC, P.O. BOX 62130, TAMPA, FL 33662. IN CANADA, AGREEMENT NUMBER 40063649, RETURN UNDELIVERABLE ADDRESSES TO NATIONAL GEOGRAPHIC, P.O. BOX 4412, STN. A, TORONTO, ONTARIO M5W 3W2. UNITED KINGDOM NEWSSTAND PRICE £5.99. REPR. EN FRANCE: EMD FRANCE SA, BP 1029, 59011 LILLE CEDEX; TEL. 320.300.302; CPPAP 0715U89037; DIRECTEUR PUBLICATION: D. TASSINARI DIR. RESP. ITALY; RAPP IMD SRL, VIA G. DA VELATE 11, 20162 MILANO; AUT. TRIB. MI 258 26/5/84 POSTE ITALIANE SPA; SPED. ABB. POST. DL 353/2003 (CONV L.27/02/2004 N.46) ART 1 C. 1 DCB MILANO STAMPA QUAD/GRAPHICS, MARTINSBURG, WV 25401. MEMBERS: IF THE POSTAL SERVICE ALERTS US THAT YOUR MAGAZINE IS UNDELIVERABLE, WE HAVE NO FURTHER OBLIGATION UNLESS WE RECEIVE A CORRECTED ADDRESS WITHIN TWO YEARS.

PHOTOS: HANS WEISE (SHIPBUILDING); MARK THIESSEN, NGM STAFF

ON THE SIDE OF SCIENCE

In the past three years, this magazine has run 34 stories on climate change—including a special issue devoted entirely to the topic.

Our commitment is ongoing. In the April issue, to mark Earth Day, we'll publish a guide that separates fact from fallacy on climate change and a feature story on how rising temperatures are affecting Alaska. Later this year we'll offer looks at the Arctic, Antarctica, the Galápagos Islands, and other places at risk as the world warms. Our television channel is airing a documentary film and a three-part series on water issues.

And that doesn't count the hundreds of climate stories we have published on *nationalgeographic.com*.

Covering our climate—where we keep setting records for the hottest year—is one of the most important things we can do. It's especially crucial in an era when some people claim that there are no "facts" and basic science is loudly questioned without embarrassment.

At *National Geographic* we are proudly nonpartisan. But there are a few matters on which we do take sides:

• We are on the side of facts.
• We are on the side of science.
• We are on the side of the planet.

We promise that we will continue to report—factually and fairly—on how climate change is altering the Earth.

Those who deny climate change receive a lot of attention, but the vast majority of Americans acknowledge the reality of the problem. Nearly two-thirds of respondents told Gallup last year that they are worried about global warming—the highest figure since 2008.

To help keep you current on developments, we're expanding our environmental coverage across publishing platforms. We'll have deeply reported magazine stories, brought to life with exceptional photography, graphics, and maps. On *nationalgeographic.com,* you'll find topical stories every day, as well as a climate change reference guide. And on our social media accounts, our contributors are providing compelling views of climate change from all points of the globe.

We are committed to understanding, and to helping you understand, how best to care for this planet. Perhaps philosopher Eric Hoffer put it best: "In a time of drastic change it is the learners who inherit the future. The learned usually find themselves equipped to live in a world that no longer exists."

Thank you for reading *National Geographic.*

Susan Goldberg, *Editor in Chief*

When Albert Lukassen was a boy in Greenland more than 50 years ago, he hunted until June on the frozen Uummannaq Fjord. Today the fjord thaws by April, when this photo was taken. The Inuit man's story appears in *National Geographic's* Climate Issue, which can be ordered at 1-800-777-2800.

WILDLIFE AS CANON SEES IT

Master of mimicry. The Sri Lanka blue magpie uses mimicked alarm calls to make other birds believe a predator is in the vicinity. As these rivals fly away, the magpie helps itself to their food. It's such a good trick that drongos have learned to imitate the magpie's call and achieve the same effect. Foraging in groups of up to seven birds, the magpie hops from branch to branch searching for crickets, caterpillars, beetles and more. But as habitat loss and fragmentation take their toll, the master's calls are fading away.

As Canon sees it, images have the power to raise awareness of the threats facing endangered species and the natural environment, helping us make the world a better place.

EOS System

Canon

Estonia
Like mushrooms sprouting in soil, wooden poles capped with ice poke free of the sea at an old port in Tallinn. Lit by the rising sun, these remnants of a dock on the Paljassaare Peninsula are visible due to an unusually low tide.

PHOTO: ANDREI REINOL

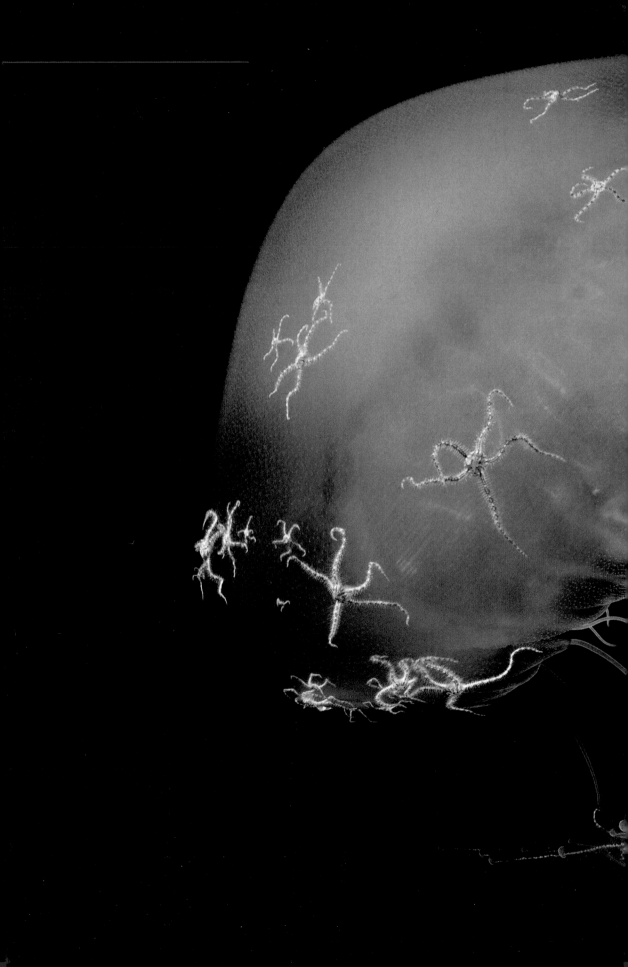

Mozambique
A drifting jellyfish plays host to a small constellation of brittle stars. Scientists aren't sure why the two invertebrate species sometimes unite. The salad-bowl-size jelly may offer the stars food, protection, or transportation.

PHOTO: ANDREA MARSHALL

England
On a misty morning in London's Richmond Park, a red deer stag bellows during mating season. From September to November, mature males roar and thrash the brush with their antlers to attract females, aka hinds, and to intimidate rivals.

PHOTO: FÉLIX MORLÁN GONZÁLEZ

Andrew Richard Hara
Hilo, Hawaii

Hara, a professional photographer, had been to the summit of Mauna Kea hundreds of times in search of a clear sky. A meteor shower in July 2014 offered cosmic dramatics. "I think being at only 60 percent oxygen helps me focus on what makes a great image," he says.

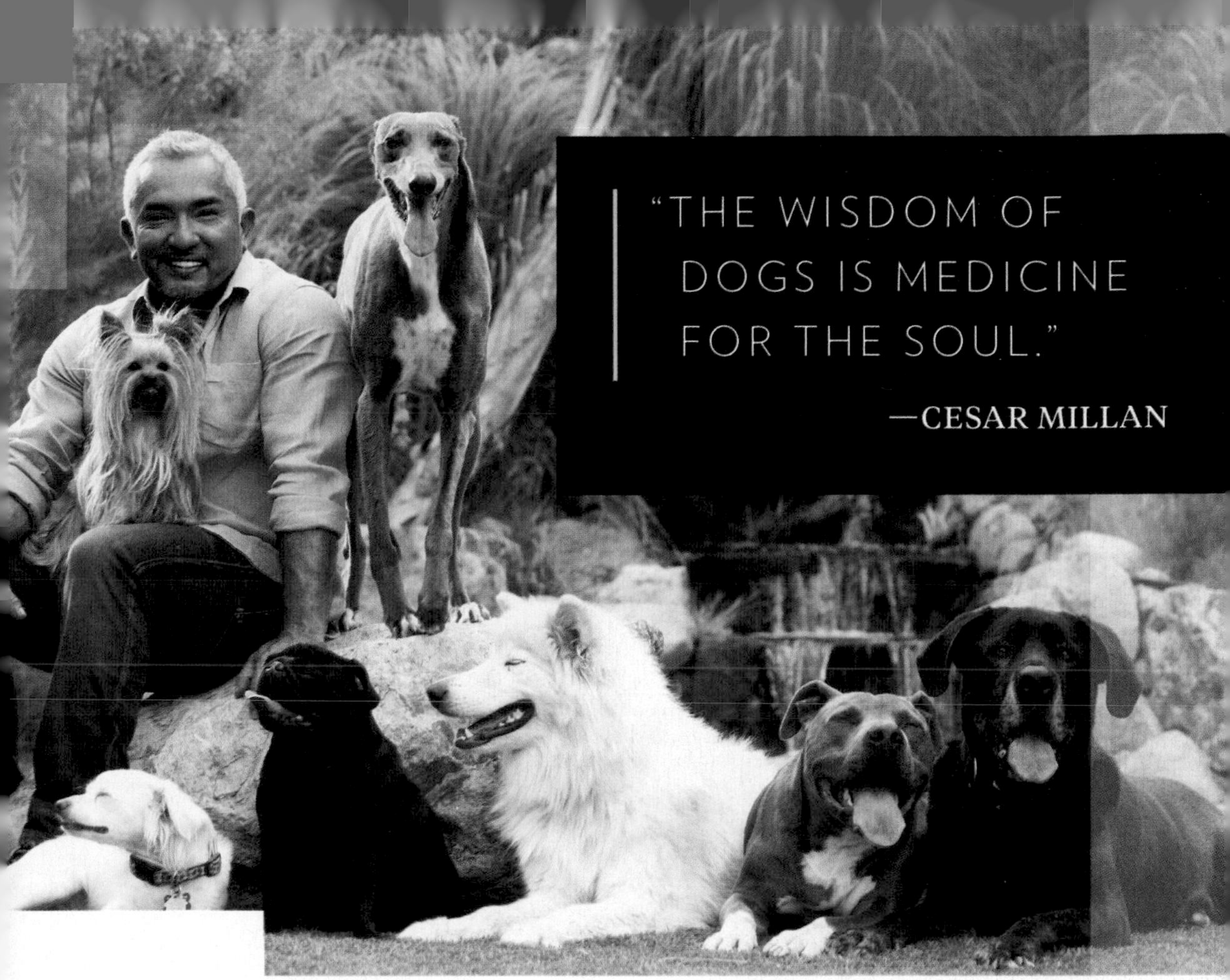

"THE WISDOM OF DOGS IS MEDICINE FOR THE SOUL."
—CESAR MILLAN

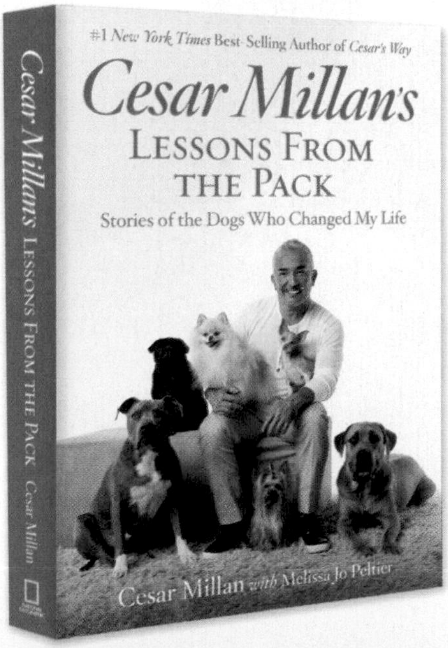

#1 New York Times Best-Selling Author of Cesar's Way
Cesar Millan's
LESSONS FROM THE PACK
Stories of the Dogs Who Changed My Life
Cesar Millan with Melissa Jo Peltier
Cesar Millan's LESSONS FROM THE PACK Cesar Millan

In this intimate narrative, best-selling author and world-renowned dog behaviorist Cesar Millan reveals the many ways man's best friend is also our greatest teacher. Sharing never-before-told insights into his own life, Cesar takes us on an emotional journey, highlighting lessons he's learned from his pack along the way. With insider observations from celebrity clients such as Kesha and Jada Pinkett Smith, Cesar offers legions of dog owners around the world a unique blueprint for happiness and fulfillment through canine camaraderie.

SIX HUNDRED MILES WITH SKIS, KITES, AND WIND

By Kat Long

On the southeastern edge of the Greenland ice sheet, a blast of Arctic wind hit the three kite-skiers. Sarah McNair-Landry's kite billowed, but with her safety latch jammed, the gust yanked her 20 feet into the air. She dropped head-first onto the ice, cracking her helmet and briefly blacking out.

The accident almost derailed her expedition with kayakers Ben Stookesberry and Erik Boomer—an expedition to kite-ski from east to northwest across Greenland. But the three continued on, wearing skis while harnessed to giant kites designed to catch the wind and propel them across 600 miles of ice.

"You've got these amazing winds and conditions in Greenland," says McNair-Landry. "You can travel so much faster and farther, especially while pulling sleds, than you would if you were just skiing." On some days the three would ski across the terrain from 3 a.m. to 10 p.m. They encountered dangerous crevasses, uneven ice, and a seven-mile ice canyon carved by meltwater.

After the canyon they paddled a wild Arctic river replete with waterfalls and bone-chilling class-five rapids to complete the journey. McNair-Landry later learned her fall had cracked a vertebra in her back, but that didn't detract from an adventure well traveled. "I love having one goal that you work toward as a team," she says, "even though there will be a lot of challenges to get there."

NATGEO.COM
/EXPLORERS

INSTAGRAM
@sarahmcnairlandry
@eboomer
@redonkulous2u

The three adventurers crossed 600 miles of Greenland's punishing terrain in 46 days.

New World
monkeys
(22 tool uses)

Bonobo
(21)

Old World
monkeys
(19)

Elephants
(12)

Rodents
(8)

Insects
(7)

Ungulates
(4)

Prosimians
(3)

Arachnids
(3)

Fish
(2)

Amphibians
(1)

ANIMAL HACKS

By Rachel Hartigan Shea

Humans aren't the only creatures to use tools. Archerfish shoot water droplets from their mouths to fell insects. Octopuses carry coconut shells to serve as shelter. Orangutans borrow canoes to forage for aquatic plants.

"Tool use is widespread and diverse,"

ALBERTO LUCAS LÓPEZ, NGM STAFF; KELSEY NOWAKOWSKI
PHOTO OF PAPER CONSTRUCTION: REBECCA HALE, NGM STAFF

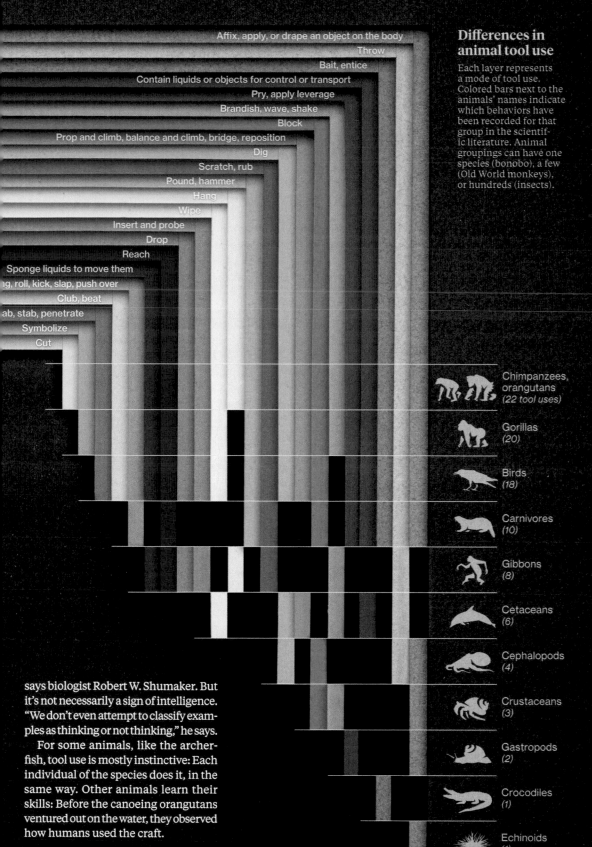

Differences in animal tool use

Each layer represents a mode of tool use. Colored bars next to the animals' names indicate which behaviors have been recorded for that group in the scientific literature. Animal groupings can have one species (bonobo), a few (Old World monkeys), or hundreds (insects).

Affix, apply, or drape an object on the body
Throw
Bait, entice
Contain liquids or objects for control or transport
Pry, apply leverage
Brandish, wave, shake
Block
Prop and climb, balance and climb, bridge, reposition
Dig
Scratch, rub
Pound, hammer
Hang
Wipe
Insert and probe
Drop
Reach
Sponge liquids to move them
ag, roll, kick, slap, push over
Club, beat
ab, stab, penetrate
Symbolize
Cut

Chimpanzees, orangutans
(22 tool uses)

Gorillas
(20)

Birds
(18)

Carnivores
(10)

Gibbons
(8)

Cetaceans
(6)

Cephalopods
(4)

Crustaceans
(3)

Gastropods
(2)

Crocodiles
(1)

Echinoids
(1)

says biologist Robert W. Shumaker. But it's not necessarily a sign of intelligence. "We don't even attempt to classify examples as thinking or not thinking," he says.

For some animals, like the archerfish, tool use is mostly instinctive: Each individual of the species does it, in the same way. Other animals learn their skills: Before the canoeing orangutans ventured out on the water, they observed how humans used the craft.

SOURCE: ROBERT W. SHUMAKER, INDIANAPOLIS ZOO

On this parchment (left), the naked eye sees only one text. But a multispectral image (right), shows two: the visible text, in red, and an earlier, erased document underneath, in blue.

RECOVERING ERASED WISDOM

By A. R. Williams

Built in the sixth century at the foot of Mount Sinai in Egypt, St. Catherine's Monastery is the world's oldest such institution in continuous use. Its library preserves hundreds of manuscripts collected during medieval times—classical texts, scriptures, and other documents of interest to the monks. But it turns out that people recycled the pages of some of those manuscripts, erasing texts they no longer needed. Since 2011 the monastery has been working to recover some of those long-lost erasures using modern digital technology.

About half of the library's manuscripts were written on parchment, the specially prepared skin of a calf, goat, or sheep. Parchment can be recycled by scraping off any ink and writing on the fresh surface. The old text isn't entirely gone, though. It remains embedded in the page as a ghostly shadow, which can be resurrected with a technique called multispectral imaging, designed to peer into both visible and invisible wavelengths of light.

So far the imaging has revealed some 6,800 hidden pages in 74 of the monastery's 163 recycled parchments, called palimpsests. "We have identified erased texts in 10 languages that date from the fifth to the 12th centuries," says Michael Phelps, the director of the recovery effort. In the example above, a text in Syriac overlays a ninth-century translation of a page from a medical treatise by the ancient Greco-Roman physician known as Galen.

With dozens of palimpsests yet to be scanned, Phelps believes there are still treasures to come: "It's not unlikely that St. Catherine's holds many more pages of previously unidentified and unstudied texts from antiquity."

HIGH-TECH TRAPPINGS

A researcher at the University of Tokyo spent six years trying to transform electrical currents into the flavor of salt. The result? A fork that fools taste buds by transmitting the sensation of salt to the tongue without a pinch of sodium.

An Israeli tech start-up is replacing bifocals with "omnifocals." The autofocusing glasses have infrared sensors that detect the distance between pupils and the object being viewed, refocusing in 300 milliseconds.

Your cell phone knows you best. Scientists at the University of California San Diego swabbed 39 devices and were able to identify their owners' grooming products, medical conditions, recently visited locations, and favorite foods. Such a composite character sketch can be used in criminal profiling or medical monitoring.

A scientist at the University of Central Florida developed a material to harvest and store the sun's energy. Woven into clothing, the copper-ribbon filament will turn a wearer into a self-charging solar battery that may someday power a phone from inside a pocket.

TRAVEL THE WORLD
WITH NATIONAL GEOGRAPHIC

UP AND OVER

By Daniel Stone

Technically it's ancient technology. But now the two-millennia-old principle of the Greek mathematician Archimedes has been deployed at gargantuan scale. The Three Gorges Dam, China's marvel on the Yangtze River, is one of the world's largest engineering projects—the product of 37 million cubic yards of concrete. Its final feature, inaugurated in late 2016, is a new ship lift, a hydraulic seesaw that raises and lowers vessels as many as 371 feet to traverse the dam.

Archimedes' notion was simple: The weight of a buoyant object is equal to the weight of water it displaces. Take two identical chambers filled with equal amounts of water. They will balance on a scale. Add an object—e.g., a ship—to one of them, and let water of an equal weight out. The two chambers will remain balanced. Remove water from one chamber, and that chamber will slowly rise.

A system designed to accommodate ships up to 3,000 metric tons is a little more complex. The dam first opened with a series of locks, similar to the Panama Canal's. The new ship lift raises and lowers boats using cables, a basin, motors—and simple gravity. Concrete counterweights in addition to water keep the system balanced, as do high-tech safety stops.

The China Three Gorges Corporation, which designed the lift with German engineers, expects several benefits: lower power needs, a rise in shipping capacity, increased passenger traffic, and lower carbon emissions—plus, the universal currency of time. A crossing that once spanned three to four hours via locks now takes just 40 minutes.

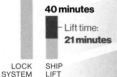

4 hours

The ship lift reduces transit times from up to four hours through the lock system to less than one hour.

40 minutes

Lift time:
21 minutes

LOCK
SYSTEM

SHIP
LIFT

THE THREE GORGES DAM

The dam was completed in 2012 after 18 years of construction. The world's largest hydropower plant, it has increased economic traffic upriver but also displaced at least 1.3 million people and caused significant ecological changes.

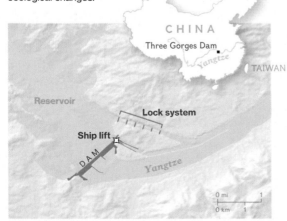

CHINA
Three Gorges Dam
Yangtze
TAIWAN
Reservoir
Lock system
Ship lift
DAM
Yangtze

0 mi 1
0 km 1

HOW IT WORKS

1. Entering the Lift

Vessels enter the ship chamber, which accommodates a draft (or depth) of almost nine feet and a height of 60 feet. The chamber can handle boats that displace a maximum of 3,000 metric tons of water, or 793,000 gallons.

JASON TREAT, NGM STAFF; KELSEY NOWAKOWSKI
ART: BRYAN CHRISTIE. SOURCES: CHINA THREE GORGES
CORPORATION; THREE GORGES NAVIGATION AUTHORITY;
KREBS+KIEFER ENGINEERS

3. Exiting the Lift
At the top of the lift, the chamber levels off with the water on the high side of the dam. A steel gate opens, and the vessel exits the chamber.

2. The Chamber Rises
The chamber is made of reinforced concrete and is suspended from 256 cables attached to counterweights. When the counterweights go down, the chamber rises.

371 feet

151 feet

433 feet

85 feet

SAFETY MEASURES
The ship chamber is accompanied up and down by four static screws, called rotary locking rods. In the event of an accident, the screws, which follow threaded tracks, are locked and the chamber becomes immobile.

COUNTERWEIGHTS
Water can be added to or subtracted from the chamber to help raise or lower it. While gravity primarily powers the lift, electric motors are used to ensure its stability and safety, much like with an elevator.

EFFECT ON TRAFFIC
Cargo traffic through the locks rose faster than expected after they opened in 2003, while passenger traffic declined. Other recent infrastructure projects, including the Yiwan Railway and the Hurong Expressway, offer faster routes for migrant workers through the Three Gorges region.

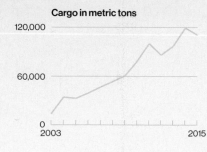

Cargo in metric tons

120,000

60,000

0

2003

2015

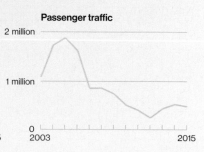

Passenger traffic

2 million

1 million

0

2003

2015

The Science of Jazz

Herbie Hancock on piano and **Wayne Shorter** on saxophone. They first paired up in the '60s, playing with the Miles Davis Quintet. Their pioneering musicianship endures, spanning two centuries. During a syncopated chat with Neil deGrasse Tyson, they drew connections between music and other matters: science, education, inspiration.

Neil deGrasse Tyson: I've got to start by saying that between the two of you there's almost 160 years of life. Wayne, you're…
Wayne Shorter: I'm 82.
NT: And Herbie?
Herbie Hancock: I'm 76.

NT: I don't know what's going on with the two of you. You look the same as when I bought your albums in the 1970s. Both of you have been at this since you were young, right?
WS: I started playing the clarinet when I was 15, taking lessons every Saturday, and then I went to the saxophone at 16. In the old days we had record gramophone players, and I would play alongside, like, Dvořák's *New World Symphony* and try to jump in where it was conducive, try to add something.

I also was listening to Charlie Parker, Dizzy Gillespie, Thelonious Monk—and playing hooky from my high school classes. When they caught me, the vice-principal had my mother and father come in and asked where I had been going. I told them, to the theater around the corner where they showed musical films with Gillespie, Parker, Lionel Hampton. So the vice-principal called the music director and put me in music class.

NT: Something like that happened to me in sixth grade. I was a little bit disruptive in class—occasionally, a lot disruptive—and all of my book reports were on astronomy. The teacher saw that and told me that the Hayden Planetarium in New York offered advanced classes in physics and math and the universe. I started taking them, and this became an outlet for my energy, a way of harnessing curiosity completely.

Herbie, at age 11 you won a piano competition?
HH: Right. It was a young people's concert series in Chicago, and if you win the contest, you get to play the concerto that you used for the audition, with the Chicago Symphony Orchestra.

There were a couple of reasons I got into music. One of them is that my mother saw that every time I would go to my best friend's apartment, the first thing I'd say is, "Hey, can I play your piano?" So she told my father, "We got to get this boy a piano." My brother and sister and I started lessons. After about three years they got interested in sports and dropped piano, but I continued because I was too little, my hands were too small—I wasn't as good at sports as others. But on the piano I was as good as anybody.

NT: When I bring my expertise to the public, I figure out a way to package it and what words to use. Then I stand up in front of an audience and deliver my astrophysics lecture. And if I succeed, people will hear it, they'll learn—and ideally they'll be enlightened by it and make it part of themselves. So that's my conduit of communication. Your conduit of communication is music.
HH: The conduit is being human and manifesting that humanity in everything that you do. Not just the thing that

Neil deGrasse Tyson is the host of the *StarTalk* television series on National Geographic. His new book is *StarTalk: Everything You Ever Need to Know About Space Travel, Sci-Fi, the Human Race, the Universe, and Beyond.* It's available wherever books are sold and at *shopng.com/startalk*.

you're famous for, the thing that you're known for being good at. We both share having played with Miles Davis [in a quintet that included bassist Ron Carter and drummer Tony Williams].

WS: And when Tony Williams was asked, "What do you think about when you're playing the drums?" he said, "If I could tell you what I was thinking about, I wouldn't have to play the drums."

NT: What you're saying is that music brings vocabulary to you that doesn't otherwise exist.

WS: *Mm-hmm.*

HH: Right. And people still continue to create new avenues within the music.

NT: I'm intrigued by the referencing that goes on in your music, both of you, to scientific themes. To the universe in particular. What role has science played in your lives?

HH: Let me just say that when I was a little kid, even before I got the piano, I was already taking watches and clocks apart and trying to put them back together, because I was always curious. That was all well and good until I tried to take apart my Lionel electric train. I got a spanking for that.

NT: It's been suggested that the next generation, their curiosity is not fostered in that way because nothing can be taken apart. You don't take apart your computer to meddle with its parts. So this whole world of the tinkerer, learning how things work, might be a lost era.

HH: There is tinkering, in music. And all kids love music. We have a new initiative that I presented formally to UNESCO called Math, Science & Music. It's using musical elements to teach math and science.

NT: We know the concept of STEM education—science, technology, engineering, and math. There's been a movement to add an *A* in there: STEAM, for science, technology, engineering, *arts,* and mathematics. I was wondering if you can reflect on the value of an arts education in our life, in our society, in our personal growth.

'I like finding artists who've been touched by the universe.'
Tyson, on Shorter (left) and Hancock

HH: We've been told that a lot of young people are not interested in math and science, but they're interested in music. Let's use what they're interested in to teach math and science—that's a win-win for the arts community, and for humanity, really.

NT: Yes.

HH: There are so many connections between music and people we revere in the scientific community. Einstein played violin.

NT: I read that John Coltrane was influenced by Einstein.

WS: And Dr. Albert Schweitzer played the organ.

HH: The scientific community created this technological age—but where did that impetus come from? If you ask many people—like Larry Page, one of the co-founders of Google—they say music was a big influence. I've privately asked many scientists if they've had a connection with music or other arts, and the answer was yes from maybe 85 percent of them.

So, if these people who have this attachment to the arts created this technological age that we're living in, then in order for it to thrive *we* need the arts the same way *they* needed the arts.

Shorter's work with Hancock and other artists is the subject of a forthcoming documentary, *Wayne Shorter: Zero Gravity.* Shorter says he gave the film that name to express "a buoyancy, a state of being which is untethered, transitory."

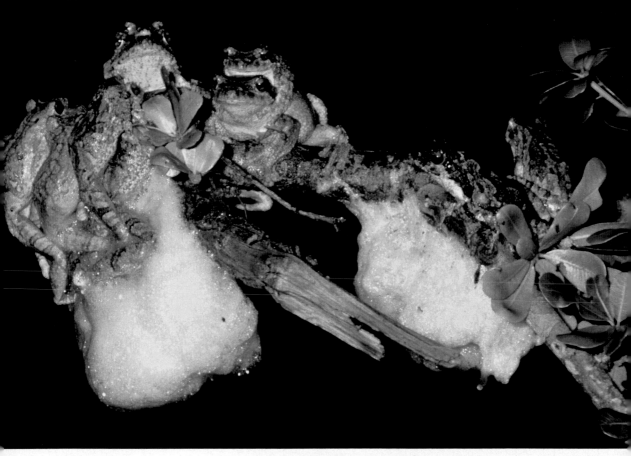

SEX THAT WORKS UP A LATHER

By Patricia Edmonds

These frogs put the "group" in "group sex"—and that helps them thrive.

Of all vertebrates, gray foam-nest tree frogs exhibit the most extreme form of simultaneous polyandry, or a female mating with multiple males, says behavioral ecologist Phillip Byrne of the University of Wollongong in Australia.

After a heavy rain swells pools in the African landscape, male frogs gather in poolside vegetation and call for mates, while females in the pools absorb water through their skin. When she's hydrated enough, a female heads for an overhanging branch. En route she is amplexed—gripped in a sexual embrace—by a male.

The joined pair climb to a nesting site. There the female discharges a watery fluid, whips it to a foam with her back legs, and puts in her eggs. At this point, says Byrne, up to 20 more males "line up in an orderly fashion by the female and vigorously and synchronously beat their back legs to help make a big wonderful nest," where they deposit their sperm.

The group spends hours pumping out gametes and bubble-wrapping them in foam that will shield growing embryos. Five days later tadpoles will wiggle free of the nest and plop into the water below.

Nearly all *C. xerampelina* females mate with multiple males to produce one egg clutch, says Byrne—and that confers genetic advantages. His research shows that 20 percent more offspring survive from those females than from females that mate with just one male.

Unlike species whose males compete brutally to mate, these frogs' orgies are calm affairs, Byrne says. "By the females' letting lots of males sire offspring, it makes this a pretty relaxed business."

GRAY FOAM-NEST TREE FROG
CHIROMANTIS XERAMPELINA

HABITAT/RANGE
Tree-, crop-, and grass-covered lands in parts of southeastern Africa

CONSERVATION STATUS
Least concern

OTHER FACTS
Polyandry makes offspring more genetically diverse. That could help insulate *C. xerampelina* from threats that have resulted in about a third of the globe's amphibian species being classified as threatened or extinct.

NEW VISIONS OF THE
VIKINGS

Yes, they were brutal. They also had women leaders, coveted riches and finery, and encountered more than 50 cultures from Afghanistan to Canada.

In a feathered helmet that's more fantasy than fact, a Shetland Islander celebrates his Viking heritage at the annual Up Helly Aa fire festival. The revelry includes torching a replica longship.

ELLIOT ROSS

Bristling with spears and swords, Viking and Slav reenactors face off in a mock battle during a festival in Wolin, Poland. What began as small raiding parties early in the Viking age grew into armies that conquered large swaths of Europe.

DAVID GUTTENFELDER

By Heather Pringle
Photographs by Robert Clark and David Guttenfelder

A cold drizzle falls as we shiver in the streets, waiting for the Viking lord and his band of raiders to appear. It's a raw January night in the old Shetland town of Lerwick, but there's euphoria in the air.

Beside me, a man with two young children laughs as he spots a red smoky haze rising behind the town hall. "Looks like they torched the whole building," he shouts, to grins all around. Fire, after all, is why we are here. It's Up Helly Aa, the great incendiary celebration of the Viking past in Shetland. Like everyone else, I've come to see a Viking ship burn.

As the lord's squad and dozens of others pour into the street, fire seethes from hundreds of torches. A roar of delight goes up from the crowd as it catches sight of the sleek longship the raiders tow. The Vikings first landed on these rocky shores north of the Scottish mainland some 1,200 years ago, crushing the local resistance and taking the land. For nearly seven centuries Norwegian lords ruled Shetland, until they finally pawned the islands to a Scottish king. Today the old Norse dialect—Norn—is all but forgotten in Shetland, but the islanders remain intensely proud of their Viking past. Each year they prepare obsessively for Up Helly Aa, assembling, plank by plank, a replica of a Viking ship.

Now, as the crowd belts out old songs of sea kings and dragon ships, the torchbearers tow the vessel into a walled field. As the lord gives the signal, a hail of torches sets the ship ablaze. Fire races up the mast, and embers fly into the night sky. On the sidewalk, children stomp their feet and dance, nearly delirious with excitement.

Later that evening, as revelers kick up their heels at parties, I marvel at the power the Vikings still hold over our imaginations. Dead and gone for centuries, these medieval seafarers

360° VIDEO

Step into the thick of Viking warfare at *natgeo.com/vikings360*.

A helmet outfitted with beardlike chain mail (right) protected a wealthy lord who lived before the Viking age, when Scandinavia was wracked by turmoil. Recent discoveries reveal that warfare wasn't the exclusive domain of Viking men. The sword above was buried with a female commander.

GABRIEL HILDEBRAND, SWEDISH HISTORY MUSEUM/CC BY (SWORD, IN TWO PIECES); ROBERT CLARK, PHOTOGRAPHED AT GUSTAVIANUM, UPPSALA UNIVERSITY MUSEUM

Historical interpreters bring a reconstructed
longhouse to life at the Ribe Viking Center in
Denmark. Meals were cooked over an open fire
on a hearth, and Viking fare included salted
herring, barley porridge, and boiled sheep heads.
DAVID GUTTENFELDER

The earliest attackers often struck monasteries brimming with treasures such as this gold pendant, from a Viking hoard unearthed in Scotland.

ROBERT CLARK, WITH PERMISSION OF HISTORIC ENVIRONMENT SCOTLAND

and warriors live on in the invented worlds of filmmakers, novelists, and comic book artists. Today most of us can reel off details of these imagined Vikings—how they fought and feasted, where they lived, how they died. But how much do we really know about the Vikings? Who were they, how did they see the world, and what were their lives truly like?

Now, with advanced technology—from satellite imagery to DNA studies and isotope analysis—archaeologists and other scientists are coming up with many surprising new answers. In Estonia, scientists are poring over two buried ships filled with slain warriors, shedding new light on the violent origins of the Vikings. In Sweden, researchers are studying the remains of a female Viking commander, illuminating the role of women in warfare. And in Russia, archaeologists and historians are tracing the routes of Viking slave traders, revealing the importance of slavery to the Viking economy. For archaeologists the doors are starting to swing open on a world that was far more complex and compelling than once thought. "These are heady times in Viking research," says Jimmy Moncrieff, a historian at the Shetland Amenity Trust in Lerwick.

Taken together, the new studies reveal a fresh picture of the ambitions and cultural impact of these daring seafarers. From the shores of their Scandinavian homeland, between the Baltic and North Seas, Viking fortune seekers took to the world stage in the mid-eighth century, exploring much of Europe over the next 300 years and traveling farther than earlier researchers ever suspected. With sleek sailing ships and expert knowledge of rivers and seas, they journeyed to what are now 37 or more countries, from Afghanistan to Canada, according to archaeologist Neil Price of Uppsala University in Sweden. En route they chanced upon more than 50 cultures and

traded avidly for luxuries. They donned Eurasian caftans, dressed in silk from China, and pocketed heaps of Islamic silver coins. They built thriving cities at York and Kiev, colonized large swaths of Great Britain, Iceland, and France, and established outposts in Greenland and North America. No other European seafarers of the day ventured so fearlessly and so far from their homeland. "It's only the people from Scandinavia who do this," says Price. "Just the Vikings."

But exploration and trade weren't the only roads to wealth. Viking raiders prowled the coasts of Britain and Europe, striking with sudden, shocking brutality. In northern France they sailed up and down the Seine and other rivers, attacking at leisure and filling their ships with plunder. Spreading terror far and wide, they extorted nearly 14 percent of the entire economy of western Europe's Carolingian Empire in exchange for empty promises of peace. Across the channel in England, sporadic raids expanded into total warfare, as a Viking army invaded and conquered three Anglo-Saxon kingdoms, leaving bodies to rot in the fields.

The Viking age, says Price, "is not for the squeamish." But how, ask researchers today, did all this mayhem begin? How and why did medieval farmers in Scandinavia become the scourge of the European continent?

IN THE NEARLY THREE CENTURIES before the raids on foreign shores began around A.D. 750, Scandinavia was wracked by turmoil, Price says. More than three dozen petty kingdoms arose during this period, throwing up chains of hill forts and vying for power and territory. In the midst of these troubled times, catastrophe struck. A vast cloud of dust, likely blasted into the atmosphere by a combination of cataclysms—comets or meteorites smashing into Earth, as well as the

Historical interpreters bring a reconstructed longhouse to life at the Ribe Viking Center in Denmark. Meals were cooked over an open fire on a hearth, and Viking fare included salted herring, barley porridge, and boiled sheep heads.

DAVID GUTTENFELDER

The earliest attackers often struck monasteries brimming with treasures such as this gold pendant, from a Viking hoard unearthed in Scotland.

and warriors live on in the invented worlds of filmmakers, novelists, and comic book artists. Today most of us can reel off details of these imagined Vikings—how they fought and feasted, where they lived, how they died. But how much do we really know about the Vikings? Who were they, how did they see the world, and what were their lives truly like?

Now, with advanced technology—from satellite imagery to DNA studies and isotope analysis—archaeologists and other scientists are coming up with many surprising new answers. In Estonia, scientists are poring over two buried ships filled with slain warriors, shedding new light on the violent origins of the Vikings. In Sweden, researchers are studying the remains of a female Viking commander, illuminating the role of women in warfare. And in Russia, archaeologists and historians are tracing the routes of Viking slave traders, revealing the importance of slavery to the Viking economy. For archaeologists the doors are starting to swing open on a world that was far more complex and compelling than once thought. "These are heady times in Viking research," says Jimmy Moncrieff, a historian at the Shetland Amenity Trust in Lerwick.

Taken together, the new studies reveal a fresh picture of the ambitions and cultural impact of these daring seafarers. From the shores of their Scandinavian homeland, between the Baltic and North Seas, Viking fortune seekers took to the world stage in the mid-eighth century, exploring much of Europe over the next 300 years and traveling farther than earlier researchers ever suspected. With sleek sailing ships and expert knowledge of rivers and seas, they journeyed to what are now 37 or more countries, from Afghanistan to Canada, according to archaeologist Neil Price of Uppsala University in Sweden. En route they chanced upon more than 50 cultures and

traded avidly for luxuries. They donned Eurasian caftans, dressed in silk from China, and pocketed heaps of Islamic silver coins. They built thriving cities at York and Kiev, colonized large swaths of Great Britain, Iceland, and France, and established outposts in Greenland and North America. No other European seafarers of the day ventured so fearlessly and so far from their homeland. "It's only the people from Scandinavia who do this," says Price. "Just the Vikings."

But exploration and trade weren't the only roads to wealth. Viking raiders prowled the coasts of Britain and Europe, striking with sudden, shocking brutality. In northern France they sailed up and down the Seine and other rivers, attacking at leisure and filling their ships with plunder. Spreading terror far and wide, they extorted nearly 14 percent of the entire economy of western Europe's Carolingian Empire in exchange for empty promises of peace. Across the channel in England, sporadic raids expanded into total warfare, as a Viking army invaded and conquered three Anglo-Saxon kingdoms, leaving bodies to rot in the fields.

The Viking age, says Price, "is not for the squeamish." But how, ask researchers today, did all this mayhem begin? How and why did medieval farmers in Scandinavia become the scourge of the European continent?

IN THE NEARLY THREE CENTURIES before the raids on foreign shores began around A.D. 750, Scandinavia was wracked by turmoil, Price says. More than three dozen petty kingdoms arose during this period, throwing up chains of hill forts and vying for power and territory. In the midst of these troubled times, catastrophe struck. A vast cloud of dust, likely blasted into the atmosphere by a combination of cataclysms—comets or meteorites smashing into Earth, as well as the

Far-Flung Realm

The seafaring Vikings made their dramatic entrance into the annals of European history by plundering the British Isles in the late eighth century. By the 11th, Viking raids, trade, exploration, and influence spanned much of the Northern Hemisphere, from North America to eastern Europe and Central Asia.

CANADA

LABRADOR
(MARKLAND)

N O R T H

To Vinland

L'Anse aux
Meadows

◻ Point
Rosee

NEWFOUNDLAND

Scandinavian
high-status
warrior

Scandinavian
high-status
woman

Metal helmets
denoted high
status. Only one
complete Viking
metal helmet
has ever been
discovered.

Swords, often
double-edged
with richly deco-
rated hilts, could
be more than
three feet long.

Chain mail armor
was worn by
Viking elites.

VIKINGS IN SCANDINAVIA

The peoples of Nor-
way, Denmark, and
Sweden — the Viking
homelands — shared
a rich seafaring tradi-
tion and class-based
social hierarchy,
with slaves, freemen,
and nobles ruled
by a succession
of competing regional
kings and chiefs.

The top of the Gokstad ship's stems didn't survive, but evidence suggests that dragon heads and metal ship vanes (similar to weather vanes) adorned other Viking ships.

Shields could be tied to the sides of the ship with ropes.

Lookout

NATIONAL GEOGRAPHIC

FERNANDO G. BAPTISTA, DAISY CHUNG, AND EVE CONANT, NGM STAFF; AMANDA HOBBS

SOURCES: VIBEKE BISCHOFF AND MORTEN RAVN, VIKING SHIP MUSEUM, ROSKILDE, DENMARK; JAMES GRAHAM-CAMPBELL, UNIVERSITY COLLEGE LONDON; NEIL PRICE, UPPSALA UNIVERSITY; KENNETH F. NORDAN, FRIENDS OF THE VIKING SHIP; *THE AGE OF THE DROMON: THE BYZANTINE NAVY CA 500-1204*, JOHN PRYOR AND ELIZABETH JEFFREYS

102.7 ft

Competing Technology

For comparison, the dromon was a ship used by the Byzantine Empire during the Viking age. With two levels of oars on each side, the dromon was faster when rowed over short distances but much slower than Viking ships when powered by sail.

The mast could be raised within minutes to take advantage of prevailing winds or lowered to improve rowing maneuverability.

The tack spar helped control the sail's front corner.

Oar-holes could be closed when under sail, sealing out water in heavy seas.

Spears

Deck (pine)

Oars

Stored weapons

Removable planks helped Vikings easily store items belowdecks.

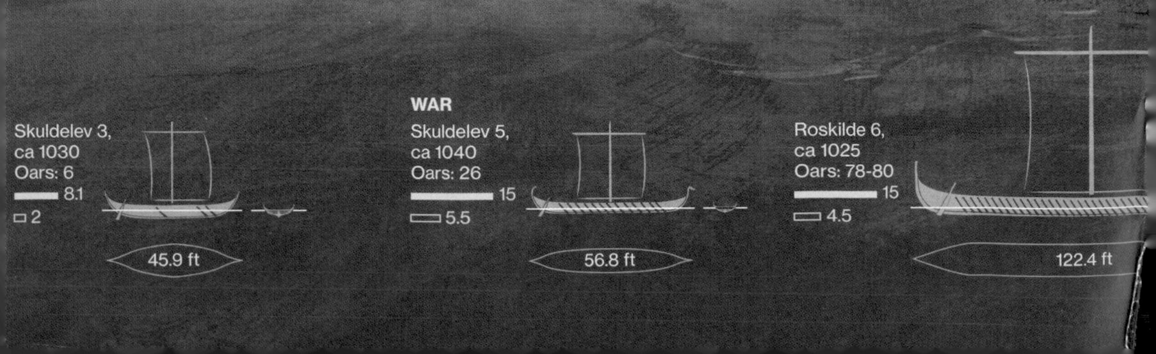

The ship was primarily constructed from oak, with the keel made from a timber almost 58 feet long.

Skuldelev 3, ca 1030
Oars: 6
8.1
2
45.9 ft

WAR
Skuldelev 5, ca 1040
Oars: 26
15
5.5
56.8 ft

Roskilde 6, ca 1025
Oars: 78-80
15
4.5
122.4 ft

GREENLAND

WESTERN
SETTLEMENT
Godthåb

AMERICA

MIDDLE
SETTLEMENT

Julianehåb • Brattahlid
EASTERN
SETTLEMENT

Labrador
Sea

Greenland S

• Hofstadir
ICELAND
Reykjavík □
Thingvellir
• Kirkjubæjarklaustur

ATLANTIC OCEAN

CONQUERING ENGLAND

In 865 Vikings landed a large army in
England. They found the Anglo-Saxon
kingdoms weak and divided, defeated
many of them, and settled in a region
that would later be called the Danelaw.

BRITISH
ISLES

Hebr

Bronze oval
brooches, often
with beads strung
between them,
fastened apron
straps. Fashions
varied by region.

Armagh •
IRISH
IRELAND
Dublin •
Limerick •

Scandinavian

Celtic Sea

Finnish

NORMANDY PEACE DEAL

After years of raids down the Seine, a deal
in 911 between the Viking warlord Rollo and
the Frankish king Charles the Simple let
the Vikings settle the coast if they would
act as a barrier against other attackers.

Portland
Vikings first
encountered in
England, 789

Gotlandic

Viking colony
914-939

Noirmouti
First raiding base
France, 84

Women hung
tools like
knives, needle
cases, and
shears from
their brooches
or belts.

Bay
Bisc

Settled Territory

*Ranges in the east are approximate. Rus settlement
in those areas was sparse, mixing with local tribes.*

Santiago de
Compostela

Gijón •

Women's
clothing could
include several
layers, with an
apron and a
shawl.

▦ by A.D. 800	⊗ Circular fort
▢ 900	⌣ Ship burial
▢ 1000	**DANES** Native Viking ethnic group

GALICIANS

First Vikin
in Spain, 8

PORTUGAL

EMIRAT
OF
CÓRDOB

Raiders, Traders, and Explorers

The underdress
was made of linen.

▦	Areas raided repeatedly during the Viking age
•	Recorded Viking attack
✕	Major battle
○	Major trade center
—	Route of exploration, plunder, or trade
▦▦	Portage area
IRISH	Ethnic group in contact with Vikings

Lisbon •

• Córdob

Niebla ✕
859
Cádiz •
Str. of Gibraltar

Seville
Medina Sidonia
Algeciras

0 mi   200
0 km   200

MOROCCO

Modern-day drainage and political boundaries are shown.

OUT OF THE NORTH

Viking culture was shaped by the unique geography of Scandinavia. While not all Scandinavians chose the life of a raider, scarce arable land and a desire to seek riches abroad drove many to the seas.

RETURNING RAIDERS

A Viking fleet nears home with slaves and other plunder in this imagined scene aboard an actual vessel — the ninth-century Gokstad ship. See photo of ship, page 41.

Sails were adopted in Scandinavia by approximately the seventh century. Only fragments survive, but evidence suggests Viking sails were roughly square shaped and made of wool dyed in bold colors or stripes to signify ownership, group identity, and status.

Sailors perched on movable storage chests while rowing.

Vikings raided for status, loot, slaves, and provisions.

Mast (pine)

Mast lock

Mast fish

Keelson

The keelson and mast fish formed a base structure for the mast and helped absorb stress while under sail. A mast lock could be removed to lower the mast.

Large stones were placed in the hull as ballast to help stabilize the ship.

Shown above
Gokstad ship, ca 895
Oars: 32
12.5
4

CARGO
Skuldelev 1, ca 1030
Oars: 4
10

1.5

5 ft

76.1 ft

51.8 ft

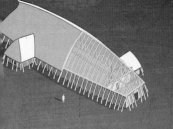

BURIAL SHIPS

Sometimes afforded to men and women of high status, ship burials could include the entombing of weapons, jewelry, expensive clothing, and sacrificial animals.

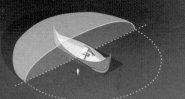

Rus man

High-status Rus woman

Married Viking women may have covered their hair.

The Rus adopted Christianity from the Byzantine Empire.

Trade with the Arab world included vast amounts of silver, often used for jewelry.

VIKINGS IN THE EAST

Swedish traders dominated Scandinavian eastward expansion from the eighth century and became leaders of the Rus, a multiethnic people who traded with the Arab and Byzantine worlds and founded merchant towns like Novgorod.

A Fearsome Fleet

Swift and deadly, the Vikings dominated the seas of northern Europe from the late eighth century to the 11th. Their ships—technological feats used for exploration, trade, warfare, and even burials—were integral to the lives of the formidable raiders. Attacking in small groups at first, fleets in the later Viking age could number 250 ships or more.

STURDY, LIGHT, AND FLEXIBLE

The Vikings built their ships starting with the keel and outer planking, only later adding internal framework and supports. This made the boats flexible and light enough for smaller ones to be transported overland.

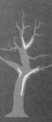

Tall, straight oak trees were favored for keels and planking. Naturally curved trees and limbs were used for frame components.

Logs were split radially with an ax to create thin but sturdy wedge-shaped planks.

Keel

D · · Mast fish

Keelson

Construction of the hull started with fore and aft stems fastened to the keel (A). Lower planking was attached with iron rivets and roves (B). Floor timbers were added to support the hull, and upper planking was added (C). The keelson (mast support) was placed on the keel. Cross-beams, knees (curved joints), and other frame components provided further reinforcement, and the mast fish was added (D).

Clinker Versus Carvel Design

Vikings used clinker design — overlapping planks fastened with rivets and roves (right). The planks were then attached to the frame with lashing. After the Viking age, large vessels were built carvel style (far right), with planks laid edge to edge.

The Gokstad ship's planking was just over one inch thick. (Shown here actual size)

CLINKER

· · · · · Lashing

Caulking
· · · · · material

Rove   · · · · · Rivet

Cask for
fresh water

Captain

Rudder

VARIETIES OF VIKING SHIPS

Early vessels were multipurpose, and
some – like the Oseberg and Gokstad
ships – were also used for burials. By the
10th century ship designs were specialized:
short, wide hulls to transport cargo and
long, narrow hulls to carry armed crews.

Speed
in knots
(1 knot =
1.15 mph)

MULTIPURPOSE
Oseberg ship,
ca 820
Oars: 30

Sailing ▬▬ 12.5
Rowing ⬜ 4

VIKING FORTS

Circular, or Trelleborg-style, forts like this one in Denmark were used for defensive and administrative purposes. They display a similar design, implying coordination by a central authority.

Circular fort at Fyrkat, Denmark

LONGHOUSES

Built of various materials including wood, stone, and turf, the Scandinavian longhouse was a large hall where inhabitants ate and slept, with additional rooms for storage.

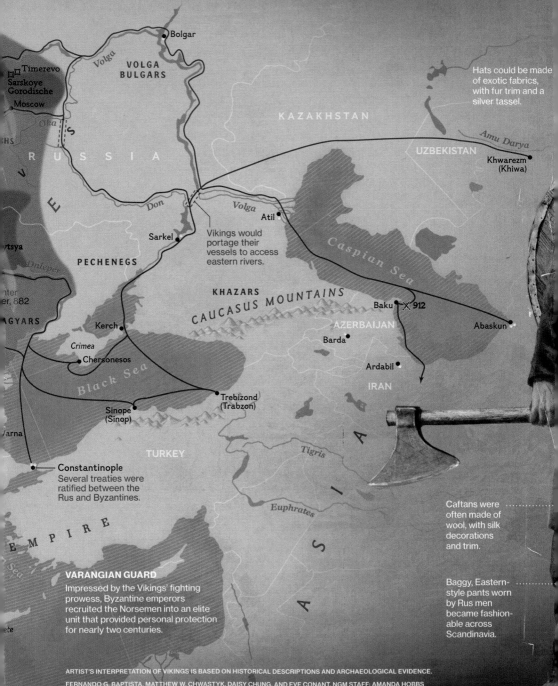

Hats could be made of exotic fabrics, with fur trim and a silver tassel.

Bolgar

Timerevo
Sarskoye
Gorodische
Moscow

VOLGA
BULGARS

Volga

KAZAKHSTAN

R U S S I A

Oka

UZBEKISTAN

Amu Darya

Khwarezm
(Khiwa)

Don

Volga

Atil

Sarkel

Vikings would portage their vessels to access eastern rivers.

PECHENEGS

Dnieper

Caspian Sea

KHAZARS
CAUCASUS MOUNTAINS

Baku ✕ 912

AZERBAIJAN

Abaskun

ter
er, 882

GYARS

Kerch

Crimea

Chersonesos

Barda

Ardabil

IRAN

Black Sea

Trebizond
(Trabzon)

Sinope
(Sinop)

Varna

TURKEY

Tigris

A
S
I
A

Constantinople
Several treaties were ratified between the Rus and Byzantines.

Euphrates

Caftans were often made of wool, with silk decorations and trim.

E M P I R E

VARANGIAN GUARD

Impressed by the Vikings' fighting prowess, Byzantine emperors recruited the Norsemen into an elite unit that provided personal protection for nearly two centuries.

Baggy, Eastern-style pants worn by Rus men became fashionable across Scandinavia.

ARTIST'S INTERPRETATION OF VIKINGS IS BASED ON HISTORICAL DESCRIPTIONS AND ARCHAEOLOGICAL EVIDENCE.

FERNANDO G. BAPTISTA, MATTHEW W. CHWASTYK, DAISY CHUNG, AND EVE CONANT, NGM STAFF; AMANDA HOBBS

SOURCES: JAMES GRAHAM-CAMPBELL, UNIVERSITY COLLEGE LONDON; NIELS LUND, UNIVERSITY OF COPENHAGEN; NEIL PRICE, UPPSALA UNIVERSITY; ANNA WESSMAN, UNIVERSITY OF HELSINKI; FEDIR ANDROSHCHUK, SWEDISH HISTORY MUSEUM

Cask for
fresh water

Captain

Rudder

CARVEL

VARIETIES OF VIKING SHIPS

Early vessels were multipurpose, and
some – like the Oseberg and Gokstad
ships – were also used for burials. By the
10th century ship designs were specialized:
short, wide hulls to transport cargo and
long, narrow hulls to carry armed crews.

Speed
in knots
(1 knot =   Sailing ━━━━ 12.5
1.15 mph)   Rowing ⊏⊐ 4

MULTIPURPOSE

Oseberg ship,
ca 820
Oars: 30

70

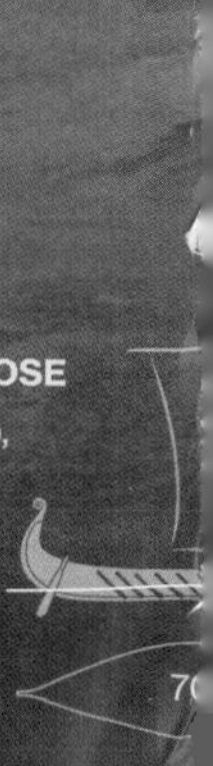

VIKING FORTS

Circular, or Trelleborg-style, forts like this one in Denmark were used for defensive and administrative purposes. They display a similar design, implying coordination by a central authority.

Circular fort at Fyrkat, Denmark

LONGHOUSES

Built of various materials including wood, stone, and turf, the Scandinavian longhouse was a large hall where inhabitants ate and slept, with additional rooms for storage.

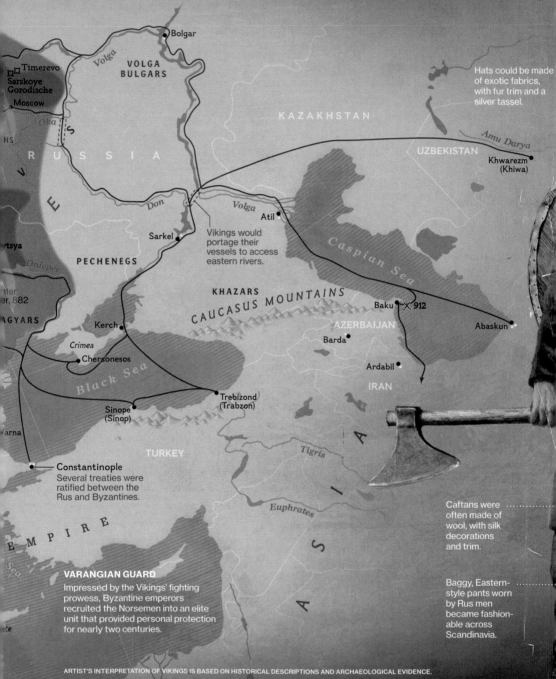

Hats could be made of exotic fabrics, with fur trim and a silver tassel.

Bolgar

Timerevo

Sarskoye Gorodische

Moscow

Volga

VOLGA BULGARS

KAZAKHSTAN

Amu Darya

UZBEKISTAN

Khwarezm (Khiwa)

R U S S I A

Oka

Don

Volga

Atil

Sarkel

Vikings would portage their vessels to access eastern rivers.

Caspian Sea

Dnieper

PECHENEGS

KHAZARS

CAUCASUS MOUNTAINS

Baku ✕ 912

Abaskun

AGYARS

nter er, 882

Kerch

Crimea

Chersonesos

AZERBAIJAN

Barda

Ardabil

IRAN

Black Sea

Sinope (Sinop)

Trebizond (Trabzon)

TURKEY

Tigris

A   S   I   A

varna

Constantinople
Several treaties were ratified between the Rus and Byzantines.

Euphrates

E M P I R E

Caftans were often made of wool, with silk decorations and trim.

VARANGIAN GUARD

Impressed by the Vikings' fighting prowess, Byzantine emperors recruited the Norsemen into an elite unit that provided personal protection for nearly two centuries.

Baggy, Eastern-style pants worn by Rus men became fashionable across Scandinavia.

ARTIST'S INTERPRETATION OF VIKINGS IS BASED ON HISTORICAL DESCRIPTIONS AND ARCHAEOLOGICAL EVIDENCE.

FERNANDO G. BAPTISTA, MATTHEW W. CHWASTYK, DAISY CHUNG, AND EVE CONANT, NGM STAFF; AMANDA HOBBS

SOURCES: JAMES GRAHAM-CAMPBELL, UNIVERSITY COLLEGE LONDON; NIELS LUND, UNIVERSITY OF COPENHAGEN; NEIL PRICE, UPPSALA UNIVERSITY; ANNA WESSMAN, UNIVERSITY OF HELSINKI; FEDIR ANDROSHCHUK, SWEDISH HISTORY MUSEUM

eruption of at least one large volcano—darkened the sun beginning in A.D. 536, lowering summer temperatures in the Northern Hemisphere for the next 14 years. The extended cold and darkness brought death and ruin to Scandinavia, lying as it did along the northern edge of medieval agriculture. In Sweden's Uppland region, for example, nearly 75 percent of villages were abandoned, as residents succumbed to starvation and fighting.

So dire was this disaster that it seems to have given birth to one of the darkest of all world myths—the Nordic legend of Ragnarök, the end of creation and the final battle, in which all gods, all supernatural beings, and all humans and other living creatures die. Ragnarök was said to begin with Fimbulwinter, a deadly time when the sun turns black and the weather turns bitter and treacherous—events that eerily parallel the dust veil that began in 536, Price says.

When summer at last returned to the north and populations rebounded, Scandinavian society assumed a new, more truculent form. Leaders surrounded themselves with heavily armed war bands and began seizing and defending abandoned territory. In this real-life *Game of Thrones,* a militarized society arose in which men and women alike celebrated the virtues of warfare— fearlessness, aggression, cunning, strength under fire. On the Swedish island of Gotland, where archaeologists have found many intact graves from this period, "almost every second man seems to be buried with weapons," notes John Ljungkvist, an archaeologist at Uppsala University.

As this weaponized society was gradually taking shape, a new technology began revolutionizing Scandinavian seafaring in the seventh century—the sail. Skilled carpenters began constructing sleek, wind-powered vessels capable of carrying bands of armed fighters farther and faster than ever before. Aboard these ships, northern lords and their restless followers could voyage across the Baltic and North Seas, exploring new lands, sacking towns and villages, and enslaving inhabitants. And men with few marriage prospects at home could take female captives as wives by persuasion or force.

All of this—centuries of kingly ambition, a

seeming abundance of wifeless young warriors, and a new type of ship—created a perfect storm. The stage was set for the Vikings to pour out of the north, setting much of Europe on fire with their brand of violence.

AROUND 750 A BAND of early Viking warriors dragged two ships onto a sandy headland on the island of Saaremaa, just off the coast of Estonia. Far from their homes in the forests near Uppsala, Sweden, the men were the bloodied survivors of a costly raid. Inside their ships lay the tangled corpses of more than 40 Viking men, including one who may have been a king. All were in their youth or prime of life—tall, muscular, strapping men—and many had seen savage fighting. Some had been stabbed or hacked to death, others decapitated. One man died after a sword took off the top of his head.

On the sandy headland the survivors began the gruesome task of reassembling severed body parts and arranging most of the dead men in the hull of the largest ship. Then they covered the bodies with cloth and raised a low, makeshift burial mound by placing their wood and iron war shields over their slain comrades.

In 2008 a work crew laying an electrical cable discovered human bones and bits of a corroded sword, and local authorities called in archaeologists. Today, sitting in his office at Uppsala University, Price marvels at the discovery. "This is the first time that archaeologists have ever been able to excavate what is clearly a Viking raid," he says. More remarkable: The warriors laid to rest at Salme, Estonia, died nearly 50 years before Scandinavian raiders descended on the English monastery of Lindisfarne in 793, long thought to have been the first Viking attack.

Today the ship burials at Salme are creating a stir among Viking specialists. "What I find amazing is all the swords," Price says. Most researchers had long assumed that early Viking raiding parties consisted of a few elite warriors armed with swords and other costly war gear, as well as a few dozen poor farm boys furnished with cheap spears or longbows. But that's clearly not the case at Salme. The burials there contained more swords than

Strung with silver ornaments and glass beads from Scandinavia and the Byzantine Empire, this colorful necklace shows the long reach of Viking traders. It was excavated from a burial mound in Gnezdovo, a busy Viking trading hub on Russia's Dnieper River.

ROBERT CLARK, PHOTOGRAPHED AT STATE HISTORICAL MUSEUM, MOSCOW

men, confirming that at least some early expeditions consisted of many warriors of high status.

ON A JANUARY MORNING in a quiet industrial park south of Edinburgh, Scotland, researchers lead the way through locked doors to a small conservation lab. For more than a year, scientists here have been unpacking the riches that one Viking leader amassed from raiding and ransacking in foreign lands. Buried some 1,100 years ago in southwest Scotland, the Galloway hoard is a collection of strange and beautiful things, from a solid-gold ingot to pieces of silk samite cloth from the Byzantine or Islamic world to an enameled Christian cross. Olwyn Owen, an independent archaeologist who specializes in the Viking age, says she's never seen anything quite like it. "It's an incredible find," she says, "just incredible."

Today a conservator has laid out some of the rarities from the hoard. On the table there's a slender gold pin shaped like a bird. It resembles an *aestel,* a small pointer that bishops and other members of the clergy once used to read sacred texts. Nearby is a gold filigree pendant, possibly designed to hold a small relic of a saint. And, at the end of the table, Owen gazes at nine silver brooches, some bearing swirling tendrils and mythical creatures, others strange humanlike faces. All but one, says Owen, were designed for Anglo-Saxon wearers. "In other words," she concludes, "some Anglo-Saxon monastery or settlement had a very bad day."

The Viking leader who carried off these treasures had a weakness for beautiful things. Rather than melting down all the plunder into bullion, this Viking lord set aside several pieces for his personal collection of exotic, foreign art. The Vikings, says archaeologist Steve Ashby with the University of York, had a taste for finer things from foreign

cultures, and some elites took pleasure in owning and using these status symbols. "The top men, they were dandies," says Ashby. "It's a society in which conspicuous consumption is important."

More Johnny Depp than Vin Diesel, Viking leaders painted their eyes, pulled on flashy colored clothing, and donned heavy jewelry—neck rings, dress pins, armbands, and finger rings. But this dress for excess had a serious purpose: Each object told a story of foreign adventure, of recklessness and courage rewarded. Fitted out in the spoils of war, a Viking was a living recruitment poster for the raiding life, beckoning young men to take an oath of loyalty in return for a share of booty. "Viking leaders couldn't be bashful about what they achieved, if they wanted to maintain a power base," Ashby says.

At the start of the Viking age, these raiders targeted mainly coastal or island monasteries—armed, it seems, with advance intelligence. Scandinavian traders were already plying the coasts of Britain and Europe, and they quickly discovered that the markets typically were held next to monasteries. Strolling past stalls and sizing up the goods, some would have spotted the silver chalices and gold altar furniture adorning monastic chapels. "I don't think it requires mental leaping to think there's someone who finally says, 'Guys, why don't we just nick the stuff?'" says Price.

Early raiding parties planned their attacks for the summer months, and they often set out with just a few ships and perhaps a hundred fighters. Bristling with iron weaponry, the raiders struck rapidly and went about the carnage swiftly, setting sail before locals could mount a defense. In France, in the ninth century alone, Viking raiders stormed more than 120 settlements, massacring monks and local inhabitants, stripping churches of their treasures, and enslaving the survivors. "If you lived in northwest France in the late ninth

Sleek wooden vessels like the Gokstad
ship were key to the success of Viking
traders and raiders. Unearthed in 1880
from a burial, the ninth-century ship
was powered by sail and 32 oarsmen.

Discovered in the grave of an elite Viking man in Sweden, this decorated horse bit, part of a bridle, was made of iron and gilded bronze. Although the Vikings are best known for their longships, the wealthy and powerful also kept prized horses.

ROBERT CLARK, PHOTOGRAPHED AT GUSTAVIANUM, UPPSALA UNIVERSITY MUSEUM

century," Price says, "you must have thought your world was ending."

As rivers of precious metals flowed back to Scandinavia, young men flocked to the great halls of Viking leaders, eager to swear their loyalty. What began as small raiding forays of two or three ships gradually evolved into fleets of 30 vessels, then many more. According to the Anglo-Saxon Chronicle, a contemporary annal, hundreds of Viking ships arrived along the east coast of England in 865, carrying a ravenous host that the Chronicle writers called *micel here,* the great army. Pushing inland along England's rivers and roads, these invaders began smashing Anglo-Saxon kingdoms and seizing large swaths of land to colonize.

Just outside the modern city of Lincoln, archaeologist Julian D. Richards from the University of York is studying one of the winter camps of the great army. The encampment, known as Torksey today, was large enough to accommodate 3,000 to 4,000 people, but discoveries there indicate that the great army was more than a fighting force. Metalsmiths melted down plunder, and merchants conducted trade. Children raced through the muddy fields, and women went about their work—which may have included leading men in battle in some parts of the Viking world.

One famous early Irish text records how a woman known as Inghen Ruaidh—or Red Girl, after the color of her hair—led a fleet of Viking ships to Ireland in the 10th century. Bioarchaeologist Anna Kjellström of Stockholm University recently reanalyzed the skeletal remains of a Viking fighter found in the old trading center of Birka, in Sweden. Mourners had furnished the grave with an arsenal of deadly weapons, and for decades archaeologists assumed that the elite fighter was male. But while studying the warrior's pelvic bones and mandible, Kjellström discovered that the man was in fact a woman.

This nameless Viking woman seems to have commanded the respect of many Viking warriors. "On her lap she had gaming pieces," says archaeologist Charlotte Hedenstierna-Jonson of Uppsala University. "This suggests that she was the one planning the tactics and that she was a leader."

THE FLEETS THAT CARRIED death and destruction to western Europe also transported slaves and commodities to markets scattered from Turkey to western Russia, and possibly Iran. Medieval Arab and Byzantine officials described convoys of armed Viking slavers and merchants known as the Rus who regularly voyaged along river routes to the Black and Caspian Seas. "I have never seen more perfect physiques than theirs," observed Ahmad Ibn Fadlan, a 10th-century Arab soldier and diplomat from Baghdad. "Every one of them carries an ax, a sword, and a dagger."

To shed light on this southern trade, archaeologists are now excavating sites along the routes to the Byzantine and Muslim worlds. On a late June morning some 230 miles southwest of Moscow, Veronika Murasheva, an archaeologist at the State Historical Museum in Moscow, walks the bank of the Dnieper River where a small medieval city once stood. Founded by Viking explorers more than 1,100 years ago, Gnezdovo lay along two major trade routes—the Dnieper, which flows into the Black Sea, and a skein of streams that sweeps into the Volga River, whose waters empty into the Caspian Sea. Gnezdovo clearly profited from this geography, flourishing and eventually sprawling over an area the size of 30 city blocks.

Today Gnezdovo is mantled in forest and grassland, but over the past century and a half, Russian archaeologists have uncovered hill forts, hoards, caches, workshops, a harbor, and nearly 1,200 burial mounds that have produced rich artifacts.

Overlooking the sea, the ruins of a Viking longhouse in the Shetland Islands recall a proud past. After defeating the local Pictish people, Viking raiders took Shetland's finest lands for their own. They brought Norse laws with them and ruled for nearly 700 years, until a Scottish king claimed the archipelago. ROBERT CLARK

Gnezdovo, they discovered, was home to a wealthy Viking elite who collected tribute from the local Slavic population and who likely managed aspects of the southern commerce. Each year, after the spring thaw, Viking traders set off from Gnezdovo in ships laden with luxury goods—furs, honey, beeswax, chunks of amber, walrus ivory—and cargoes of human slaves. Many, says Murasheva, were bound for the Black Sea and Constantinople, the capital of the Byzantine Empire and a city of more than 800,000 people at the time. In the heat and dust Viking traders wandered the markets, striking deals for their cargo and buying prized commodities: amphorae filled with wine and olive oil, fine glassware, colorful glazed plates, swatches of silk and other rare textiles.

Other Viking traders ventured farther east from Gnezdovo, following streams that wended across western Russia into the Volga. In bazaars along the river and around the Caspian Sea, Muslim buyers paid handsomely for foreign slaves, since the Quran forbade believers from owning freeborn Muslims. The eastern buyers settled their bills with heaps of silver coins known as dirhams, a key source of wealth in the Viking world.

By searching archaeological reports and databases, Marek Jankowiak, a medieval historian at Oxford University, has found records of more than a thousand hoards of dirhams that Viking traders and others buried across Europe. Based on an initial analysis, Jankowiak estimates that Viking slavers could have sold tens of thousands of eastern European, mostly Slavic, captives into bondage in the 10th century alone, earning millions of silver dirhams—an immense fortune at the time. In the Viking world, where lords regularly rewarded their fighting men with gifts of silver, the road south was the road to power.

IN THE FIRELIT HALLS of the Norse lords, storytellers also described early voyages to the west. Gazing around at those assembled, they told the tale of a trader, Bjarni Herjólfsson, who lost his way in thick fog while sailing from Iceland to Greenland. When the mist finally lifted, Herjólfsson and his men spied a new land that bore little

Viking warriors fought for riches and reputation with swords such as this (right), discovered at Gnezdovo, Russia. Warriors often chopped plunder into pieces of precious metal that could be used like currency to make purchases. But some Viking warriors valued the treasures they stole for their beauty – and as coveted status symbols. These Anglo-Saxon brooches (above) and this gold, bird-shaped pin (below) were discovered in a hoard buried by a wealthy Viking in Scotland.

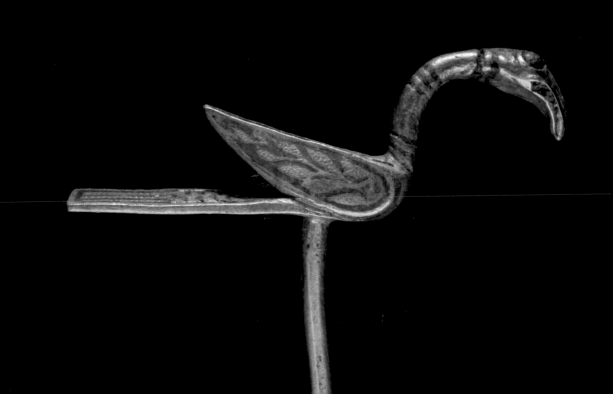

Camping under canvas as Viking armies once did, participants at the Slav and Viking Festival in Poland tend to be sticklers for authenticity. Many adorn their bodies with tattoos, and some adopt a Viking diet, slaughtering and roasting game.

DAVID GUTTENFELDER

Reenactors in Poland don armor in preparation for close combat. The Vikings lived up to their violent reputation: From an early age Scandinavian boys were trained for battle and socially conditioned for bloodshed.

DAVID GUTTENFELDER

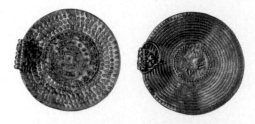

Crafted by a skilled goldsmith on the Swedish island of Gotland, these delicate pendants were designed for wealthy women. The Vikings wore mainly silver; gold pieces would have been rare and treasured.

ROBERT CLARK, PHOTOGRAPHED AT SWEDISH HISTORY MUSEUM (TWO PHOTOS)

resemblance to Greenland. It was blanketed in forest, but Herjólfsson had little interest in exploring it, so he angled his ship out to sea. The lost Viking had reached the New World by accident—the first European, it seems, to lay eyes on its shores. It was the beginning of Viking voyages to North America.

Today few feats of Viking seafarers are so cloaked in mystery and controversy as their exploration of the New World. According to the Norse sagas, Viking mariners sailed westward from Greenland in four major expeditions, searching for timber and other resources. Scouting along the northeast coast of Canada as early as 985, they wintered in small base camps, cut timber, picked wild grapes in a place they called Vinland, gave birth, and traded and fought with the indigenous people.

In 1960 a famous Norwegian explorer, Helge Ingstad, went looking for these Viking camps. Along Newfoundland's northern tip, at a place known as L'Anse aux Meadows, a local landowner led him to several hills whose contours resembled longhouses. Nearby lay a peat bog that contained bog iron, a source of iron ore prized by Vikings. Excavations revealed three large Viking halls, some huts, a furnace for processing bog iron, and butternuts from a type of tree that grows hundreds of miles farther south. Taken together, the discoveries and saga clues strongly suggested that Viking explorers not only had landed in Newfoundland but also had ventured farther south into the Gulf of St. Lawrence.

More recently a Canadian archaeologist turned up traces of Viking traders in the Canadian Arctic. Patricia Sutherland, an adjunct professor at Carleton University in Ottawa, was searching through old collections at the Canadian Museum of History near Ottawa when she discovered pieces of Viking yarn. Spun by skilled weavers, the yarn came from sites inhabited by the Dorset,

a Paleo-Eskimo people who lived in the Arctic until the 15th century. "I thought it just can't be," Sutherland says, so she expanded her museum search and discovered a trove of Viking artifacts, from whetstones for sharpening metal knives to tally sticks for tracking trade transactions.

The most intriguing find was a small stone vessel that looked like a crucible for melting metal. Sutherland and a small team recently took a closer look using a scanning electron microscope. Along the inner surface they detected traces of bronze, as well as tiny glass spheres that form when minerals are melted at high temperatures—tantalizing evidence of Viking-style metalworking. Sutherland thinks that Viking seafarers from Greenland voyaged to the Canadian Arctic to trade with indigenous hunters, exchanging metal knives and hones for thick arctic-fox furs and walrus ivory—luxury goods for European markets.

Tracking down other Viking expeditions mentioned in the sagas, however, remains a big challenge. To locate potential sites, archaeologists must comb thousands of miles of remote coastline. So three years ago archaeologist Sarah Parcak of the University of Alabama at Birmingham decided to try a new approach.

Parcak, a National Geographic fellow, specializes in using imagery from orbiting satellites to detect potential archaeological sites. In a test run in Iceland, she and her colleagues detected what appeared to be turf walls. When archaeologist Douglas Bolender of the University of Massachusetts Boston went to investigate the area, he discovered buried remnants of turf buildings and a turf wall only six inches tall—exactly where Parcak suggested. "This is astounding," he marvels, "the tiny remains of a buried turf wall identified from 770 kilometers in space."

Buoyed by this success, Parcak and her team began poring over satellite imagery of Atlantic

Still standing a thousand years after it was raised, the rune stone at Anundshög in Sweden commemorates the love of a Viking father for his son, Heden. The young man's fate is unknown, but like many young Vikings of his time, he may have immigrated to a Viking colony in eastern or western Europe. ROBERT CLARK

Canada. In southwestern Newfoundland they spotted clusters of what looked like turf walls on a promontory known as Point Rosee. Overlooking the Gulf of St. Lawrence, Point Rosee lies along a sea route to lands of butternut trees and wild grapes. And like L'Anse aux Meadows, it adjoins a large peat bog where Viking seafarers could have collected iron ore.

During a small excavation in 2015, Parcak and her colleagues found what looked like a turf wall, as well as a large hollow where someone seemed to have collected bog ore for roasting—the first step in producing iron. But a larger excavation last summer cast serious doubt on those interpretations, suggesting that the turf wall and accumulation of bog ore were the results of natural processes. Today Parcak is waiting for additional test results to clarify the picture.

Parcak thinks, however, that she and her team are developing a scientifically rigorous way to seek Viking sites in North America. Her colleague Karen Milek, an archaeologist at the University of Aberdeen, agrees. "Looking for the Norse here is

like looking for a needle in a haystack," Milek says. Satellite imagery is one of the best ways to go, she adds, "and Sarah is defining that best approach."

ON A BLUSTERY WINTER DAY, I catch a cab to Shetland's Sumburgh Airport. It's the morning after Up Helly Aa, and few Shetlanders are awake after the long night of revelry. The swords and helmets are put away, and the children are sleeping, dreaming of sea kings. The wooden longship, the pride of the lord, is now ashes in the field.

But the idea of the Vikings, the romance of these intrepid northerners who built great ships and sailed ice-choked seas to a new world and winding rivers to the bazaars of the East, never grows old, never grows tired. It lives on here and across their northern realm, a message from a long-dead world, an enduring spirit of an age. □

Science writer **Heather Pringle** is the author of three books, including *In Search of Ancient North America*. Her assignments often lead to memorable encounters with both the living and the dead.

BRISTLECONE PINES
INYO NATIONAL FOREST, CALIFORNIA

The Wisdom of
TREES

They inspire us, comfort us, and remind us how life moves on.

Convinced that tree rings could reveal Earth's climate history, scientist Edmund Schulman spent summers out West hunting the oldest living specimens. He found them in the gnarled, diminutive bristlecone pines. In 1957 Schulman discovered Methuselah, a bristlecone with 4,789 rings. (The ancient tree still stands, its location a guarded secret.) In 1964 another researcher was coring a spectacular specimen in Nevada to determine its age, when the drill bit broke. After the tree was cut down for study and its rings were found to total 4,862, scientists realized that they had unwittingly felled what was then the oldest tree known.

THE CHILD-GIVING GINKGO
TOKYO, JAPAN

Tradition holds that this tree, which stands in the courtyard of the Zoshigaya Kishimojin Temple in Tokyo, brings fertility to worshippers. Though the goddess Kishimojin is a guardian deity of children, her backstory paints a darker picture. She fed her own offspring—possibly thousands—by devouring the children of others. To teach her a lesson, Buddha hid one of her children in an alms bowl. A distraught Kishimojin appealed to him, and he admonished her for the suffering she had caused. Suitably chastened, she vowed henceforth to protect all children.

BY **CATHY NEWMAN**
PHOTOGRAPHS BY **DIANE COOK**
AND **LEN JENSHEL**

Every tree tells a story, but some are beyond eloquent, holding memories, embodying belief, marking sorrow. We hold trees in our imagination, where they grow in strange, wonderful ways in forests inhabited by fantasy and also by our fears. In fable and legend, a forest shelters spirits, witches, and once upon a time, a big bad wolf.

Also white harts that leap just ahead of the hunter's arrow, and a hermit who may emerge just in time to nudge along a tale that ends happily ever after, but sometimes not.

We incorporate the rich metaphors that trees provide: We turn over a new leaf and branch out; ideas blossom and bear fruit. Though our momentum is sapped, our resolve remains deep-rooted, and yet there are times when we can't see the forest for the trees.

Trees inspire, not just through language, but through ideas. Surely the most notable coordinates in the atlas of inspiration converge in front of a tree—an apple tree, surrounded by a wicket fence, in an orchard in Lincolnshire, England. There, reputedly, in 1666, an apple fell and prompted a young man named Isaac Newton to wonder: Why would that apple always descend perpendicularly to the ground?

The spidery script of an 18th-century account in the archives of the Royal Society in London relates that Newton was home from Cambridge (plague had closed the university) when he stepped into the garden and into a reverie. Wrote his friend and biographer William Stukeley: "The notion of gravitation came into his mind ... occasion'd by the fall of an apple, as he sat in a contemplative mood."

It was not the first eureka moment associated with a tree. Hadn't Buddha reached enlightenment while meditating under the bodhi tree? Trees invite dreaminess. A tale told in many cultures recounts how a monk, listening to a bird sing in the woods, discovered that in a blink of time, hundreds of years had flown by. And after dipping his madeleine in tea made from the flowers of a linden, Marcel Proust's narrator fell into a "remembrance of things past" in the novel of the same name.

Trees are nature's memory stick, even at the molecular level. "Each growth layer that they put on every year contains a bit of the air from that year, transformed into carbon, and so the tree physically holds the years and years of the life of the city," Benjamin Swett, author of *New York City of Trees,* said in a radio interview.

Some memories sicken the heart, like those summoned by the chestnut that stood outside the house at 263 Prinsengracht, Amsterdam, where young Anne Frank and her family hid from the Nazis. From an attic window, the only one not blacked out, Anne could watch a tree mark the seasons before the Gestapo dragged her and her family away on August 4, 1944.

"How could I have known how much it meant to Anne to see a patch of blue sky ... and how important the chestnut tree was for her," her father said years later, after reading her diary. Anne Frank died of typhus in Bergen-Belsen concentration camp in February 1945. She was 15 years old. The tree—weakened by disease—was felled during a violent rainstorm in 2010.

Some memories are collective, like those of innocence and loss embodied in another tree—the tree of the knowledge of good and evil in the Garden of Eden. It bore an apple of temptation, and there was hell to pay for its consumption.

If the dark side of the human condition can be said to originate under a tree, then it is fitting that its green shade offers consolation, like

■ **Society Grant** Your National Geographic Society membership helped fund this photo project.

NEWTON'S APPLE TREE
LINCOLNSHIRE, ENGLAND

The apple that fell from the tree in front of Sir Isaac Newton's childhood home, Woolsthorpe Manor, did not, as myth suggests, smack the great man on the head. It landed, as apples do, on terra firma. But as an account published in 1752 said, it prompted a reverie that in time crystallized into the law of gravity. A storm felled the original "gravity" tree around 1820, but it remained rooted and regrew into the tree pictured above.

that provided by an American elm embraced by a low granite wall in Oklahoma City. On April 19, 1995, a blast planned and carried out by Timothy McVeigh, a disaffected veteran, destroyed the nine-floor Alfred P. Murrah Federal Building in the center of the city, incinerating cars and claiming 168 lives.

It also scorched the trunk, sheared off the leaves, and embedded debris in a nearly 35-foot-tall elm growing in a nearby parking lot. Today the "survivor tree" is a feature of the Oklahoma City National Memorial and Museum, and it provides solace to those like Doris Jones, whose 26-year-old daughter, Carrie Ann Lenz,

pregnant at the time, perished in the explosion. "It comforts me to look at it," Jones said. "Something good survived something so bad."

Today the elm is more than 40 feet high, with a 60-foot-wide crown. By November, most of its gilded leaves have fallen. In January it is skeletal and bare. April brings the tender green of renewal, and in June it is fully dressed for summer. And so the celestial clock reverberates in the seasonal cycle of a tree whose branches bear the fruit of hope.

"It's as if that tree had a will to survive," said Mark Bays, an urban forester for the state who helped it recover. "It understood, when none of us understood, that it needed to be around." □

BOAB TREE
DERBY, AUSTRALIA

The squat, bulbous boab has provided water, food, medicine, shelter, even burial crypts for Aboriginals, some of whom regard the tree as sacred. This boab in Western Australia is known as the Derby prison tree—erroneously, according to University of Tasmania historian Kristyn Harman and University of Adelaide architectural anthropologist Elizabeth Grant. Though the tree was reputed to be a holding cell or staging area for Aboriginal prisoners en route to Derby, Harman and Grant debunk the story as "a deliberate move to present it as a dark tourism site displaying colonial triumphs over Aboriginal people."

PEAR 'SURVIVOR TREE'
9/11 MEMORIAL

NEW YORK, NEW YORK

After the conflagration of 9/11 reduced the 110-story World Trade Center towers in Lower Manhattan to metal carcasses, after a day of black smoke and ghostly ash, after the horror of 2,753 dead, the last living thing pulled from the wreckage was a Callery pear tree. It became an exemplar of the botany of grief, but also of resiliency. The tree was scarred on one side (at left, above) — the side chosen to face the main walkway used by visitors. "So they could see the moment when the world changed," said Ronaldo Vega, the memorial's former senior director of design.

MONTEZUMA CYPRESS
SANTA MARÍA DEL TULE, OAXACA, MEXICO

Sixth-grade children from the Colegio Motolinía de Antequera line up in front of a Montezuma cypress known as el Árbol del Tule. The trunk, 119 feet in circumference and roughly 38 feet in diameter, supports a crown the size of almost two tennis courts. In the 1990s the Mexican government rerouted the Pan-American Highway and approved a grant to dig a well for the tree to mitigate damage caused by car exhaust and a falling water table.

NEEM TREE
VARANASI, INDIA

In northern India the neem tree is known as the curer of all ailments and a manifestation of the Hindu goddess Shitala, a mother figure. To neighborhood residents who worship the tree at the Nanghan Bir Baba Temple, in Varanasi, it is that and more. "My son was born premature ... The doctor told us he would surely die," one man told David Haberman, a professor of religion at Indiana University, who recorded the story. "But I prayed to this neem, and ... he lived." The tree is dressed in cloth and wears a face mask of the goddess to strengthen the connection between her and worshippers.

QUAKING ASPEN
FISHLAKE NATIONAL FOREST, UTAH

Though it sounds like the heavy in a grade B science fiction flick, the Pando clone, made up of 47,000 tree trunks covering 106 acres and weighing some 13 million pounds, is real. It's a single organism, a quaking aspen that began life as a single seed—possibly tens of thousands of years ago—and spread by sending up shoots from an expanding root system. (Pando is Latin for "I spread.") Each trunk is genetically identical and no more than 150 years old, but the root system may be the oldest living organism on the planet.

MANGO TREE
NAUNDE, MOZAMBIQUE

A mango tree in Naunde, Mozambique, provides more than just shade from the sub-Saharan sun. Like other so-called palaver trees, it's a traditional setting for storytelling, ceremonies, and regulating village life. "A place to meet and talk, to seek compromise and settle disputes, to bridge differences and foster unity," wrote Kofi Annan, the former secretary-general of the United Nations, from Ghana, in his memoir. "If you have a problem and can't find a solution, you meet again tomorrow and you keep talking."

A SEA'S FADING BOUNTY

Amid a power play by China, a great fishery is at risk.

A worker uses a mallet to dislodge frozen tuna aboard a Chinese cargo vessel docked at the port of General Santos, in the Philippines. Overfishing, compounded by a maritime dispute, has caused fish populations in the South China Sea to plummet.

Marlin and other high-value fish, such as tuna, are increasingly hard to find in the South China Sea. The failure of one of the world's great fisheries would jeopardize the livelihood and food security of millions of people.

BY **RACHAEL BALE**
PHOTOGRAPHS BY **ADAM DEAN**

One time Christopher Tubo caught a 660-pound blue marlin in the South China Sea. That was years ago, when the fishing there was good, he says. He would come home from a trip with dozens of valuable fish like tuna and a haul of other species. "Here there's none of that," he says, looking toward the Sulu Sea, where he's been fishing for the past four years. His two boats, traditional Filipino outriggers called *bancas,* float in the shallow water nearby, baking in the sun.

Tubo sits on a wooden bench in front of his home, which is perched on stilts above the bay. One of his four kids wraps an arm around his leg. Worn T-shirts and shorts flutter on clotheslines behind them. Glancing at his wife, Leah, and the other children, he says, "It's just chance, whether or not we can feed our families now."

Tubo lives in Puerto Princesa, a city of 255,000 on Palawan, a long finger of an island that faces the Sulu Sea and the Philippine archipelago to the east and the contested South China Sea to the west. He's one of the more than 320,000 fishermen in the Philippines who have traditionally made their livelihood from the South China Sea—and one of a growing number who are now fishing in other, less ecologically rich waters.

That's because about eight years ago China took a more assertive posture in the region, ramping up its intimidation of other fishermen and eventually building military installations on contested islands. It was after a Chinese coast guard vessel attacked a friend's boat with water cannons that Tubo quit fishing the South China Sea. "One minute you'll see an airplane, then there's a naval boat," he says. "If we keep going over there, maybe we won't be able to go home to our families."

Tubo's decision is a reflection of the rising tensions in the region, which have ignited an increasingly fierce competition for natural resources, among other things. Encompassing 1.4 million square miles, the South China Sea is of critical economic, military, and environmental

significance: Some $5.3 trillion in international trade plies its waters annually. It is richer in biodiversity than nearly any other marine ecosystem on the planet, and its fish provide food and jobs for millions of people in the 10 surrounding countries and territories.

Of those, seven—Brunei, China, Indonesia, Malaysia, the Philippines, Taiwan, and Vietnam—have competing claims. If a military conflict were to break out, it could involve two world powers, China and the United States, a longtime ally of the Philippines. That's why the dispute has commanded worldwide attention.

Another serious yet less publicized threat looms: overfishing. The South China Sea is one of the world's most important fisheries, employing more than 3.7 million people and generating billions of dollars every year. But after decades of free-for-all fishing, stocks are dwindling, threatening the food security and economic growth of the rapidly developing nations that rely on them.

China asserts a right to almost the entire sea. It has demarcated a broad area that it says has historically been China's but that under international law includes the waters of other nations. Every other country in the South China Sea dispute, including the Philippines, bases its claims on the United Nations Convention on the Law of the Sea, the international pact that defines maritime zones and first went into effect in 1994.

In 2013 the Philippines brought a case against China before a tribunal at the Permanent Court

A Filipino fisherman wades to shore with part of his crew's catch. Yellowfin tuna (below) arrive at the fish port in General Santos, which is called the tuna capital of the Philippines. The South China Sea produces more fish than almost anywhere else, but that may not be the case for much longer.

A fisherman (above) carries a marlin caught in the South China Sea, where international disputes have whetted competition for dwindling resources. Conversely, competition for fish has exacerbated the disputes. On this occasion (below) Filipino fishermen chose to stay in national waters.

The lights on the *Melissa,* a Filipino boat, attract fish toward the vessel and up to the surface. Filipino, Chinese, Vietnamese, and Taiwanese fishermen all ply these waters, which are virtually unregulated. A Filipino man (below) fixes his net in a fishing community in Puerto Princesa.

Workers at the Navotas Fish Port Complex, the largest in the Philippines, sort the take from boats that have returned from the South China Sea. Fish are a major protein source for people in the region, so a collapse of the fishery could be disastrous.

TROUBLED WATERS

Under international law, coastal countries are entitled to maritime rights — including the authority to explore and exploit natural resources — within 200 nautical miles of their shores. But these exclusive economic zones, or EEZs, can be hotly contested in areas such as the South China Sea, where nations are densely packed and nautical claims and entitlements can overlap.

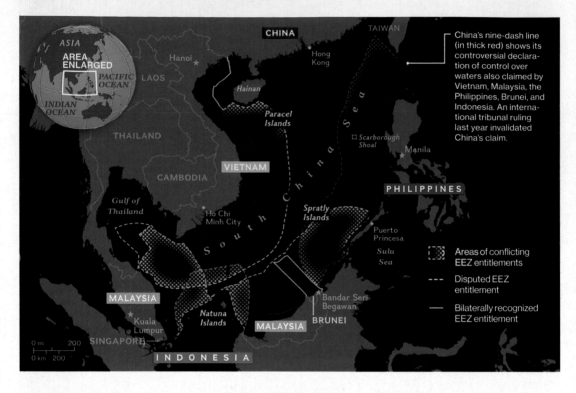

China's nine-dash line (in thick red) shows its controversial declaration of control over waters also claimed by Vietnam, Malaysia, the Philippines, Brunei, and Indonesia. An international tribunal ruling last year invalidated China's claim.

Areas of conflicting EEZ entitlements

--- Disputed EEZ entitlement

— Bilaterally recognized EEZ entitlement

of Arbitration, a forum for settling international disputes, in The Hague. China refused to participate. On July 12, 2016, the tribunal ruled in favor of the Philippines on almost all its claims, declaring that China had forfeited the possibility of any historically based rights when it ratified the UN convention in 1996. China vowed to ignore the tribunal's ruling.

THIS DISPUTE over the South China Sea intensifies competition among fishermen, and the resulting scramble for fish inflames the debate. Today some waters have less than one-tenth of the stocks they had six decades ago.

"What we're looking at is potentially one of the world's worst fisheries collapses ever," says John McManus, a marine ecologist at the University of Miami who studies reefs in the region. "We're talking hundreds and hundreds of species that will collapse, and they could collapse relatively quickly, one after another."

When coastal waters became depleted, many fishermen ventured beyond national limits and into disputed areas to make a living. Meanwhile China began bolstering its claims by aggressively supporting its fishermen. It has consolidated the coast guard, militarized fishing fleets, and promoted its subsidies for fuel and better boats. There's even a subsidy specifically for Chinese fishermen to work the waters around the contested Spratly Islands, more than 500 miles to the south of China's southernmost point (a port on the island of Hainan).

"The only reason that smaller [Chinese] fishermen go out to the Spratlys is because they're paid to do so," says Gregory Poling, with the Center for Strategic and International Studies, a Washington, D.C.-based think tank. The aggressive move by the Chinese has sped up the depletion of fish stocks, he says.

The Chinese also are building artificial islands atop reefs in the Spratlys to support military

JON BOWEN, NG STAFF
SOURCE: ASIA MARITIME TRANSPARENCY INITIATIVE, CENTER FOR STRATEGIC AND INTERNATIONAL STUDIES

installations there. "Possession is nine-tenths of the law," says Zachary Abuza, an expert on Southeast Asian politics and maritime security at the National War College, in Washington, D.C. "China is trying to enforce its sovereignty through the construction of these islands and by denying other countries access to natural resources."

Eugenio Bito-onon, Jr., is a former mayor of the Kalayaan municipality that includes islands in the Spratlys. An outspoken advocate for the Philippines' claims, he has seen firsthand how China uses its fishermen to strengthen its claim to the region. I met Bito-onon in the municipality's cramped satellite office in Puerto Princesa, where the wall of one room displays a large map of the South China Sea marked up with handwritten labels and colored dots showing which countries claim which features.

He pulled up Google Earth on his laptop and found Thitu Island, in the Spratlys, where some 200 Filipinos, including a small number of troops, live part-time, their presence demonstrating his country's claim to the island. Bito-onon pointed out just how close Chinese-claimed Subi Reef is to Thitu. So close, he said, that on a clear day residents can see it on the horizon.

Even closer are Chinese that he says have fished the reefs empty. "For the past three years, Chinese fishing boats come and go, replacing each other," he told me, adding that the boats are always within sight of the island.

AS LONG AS the conflict in the South China Sea continues, it will be nearly impossible to regulate fishing. "It's unclear whose laws you're enforcing when you have seven overlapping sets of fisheries laws," Poling says. "States have a vested interest in purposely violating fishing laws of other states." That's because abiding by another nation's fishing law amounts to accepting that nation's jurisdiction over the region.

When one country tries to protect its fishing grounds, tensions flare. In 2012 a Philippine Navy warship tried to arrest Chinese fishermen at Scarborough Shoal, about 138 miles from the Philippine coast, on suspicion of illegal fishing and poaching rare corals, giant clams, and sharks. A Chinese coast guard ship intervened to prevent the arrests, forcing a standoff. Ten weeks later both sides agreed to withdraw, but after the Philippine warship left, China's ship remained, effectively seizing control of the shoal.

Because of overfishing, fishermen have seen their catches—and the fish themselves—getting smaller, setting off a dangerous cycle. Some Filipino fishermen have resorted to perilous, illegal fishing methods, including blast fishing with homemade bombs, and cyanide fishing, which uses the poison to stun and slow the fish to make them easier to catch. Both practices kill coral and other fish, collateral damage that's pushing the sea closer to an overfishing crisis.

More destructive to the reefs, however, are China's island-building and giant clam poaching, happening on a large scale. The poaching, which entails digging up entire areas of reef to get to the clams, has caused most of the documented reef destruction in the sea. That in turn affects fish stocks. When a reef is destroyed, the ecosystem unravels. Reef fish lose their habitat, pelagic fish such as tuna lose an important source of food, and fish larvae from one reef can no longer replenish fish on other reefs.

"It's quite possible we're seeing a serious decline in about half the reefs" in the South China Sea, McManus says. "It's just total destruction."

Experts say that cooperative regional management, including dramatic cutbacks in the number of fishing boats and restrictions on certain fishing methods, would go a long way toward making the South China Sea fishery sustainable. But Poling questions whether such a plan could be devised in time to prevent the fishery from collapsing.

"What that requires is setting aside the disputes," Poling says. "It's possible. It's just not likely. To have a successful joint management system, the first step is to agree on what area you're talking about." If China clings to its expanded jurisdictional claim while other countries base their claims on international law, agreement won't be possible, he says.

And so, the South China Sea's fish—its principal resource—are disappearing, even as nearby countries stand passively by or encourage their fishermen to keep taking more. □

This is the debut of **Dispatches,** a series of field reports from National Geographic writers and photographers. This story was produced by National Geographic's Special Investigations Unit, with grants from the BAND Foundation and the Woodtiger Fund. Aurora Almendral provided additional reporting.

A Fight to Survive

On their Indonesian island, crested black macaques are hunted for meat, kept as pets, and threatened by a shrinking habitat. Can they be saved?

A crested black macaque hangs out beachside in a nature reserve on Sulawesi. In studying these intriguing monkeys, known locally as *yaki*, scientists are learning how their social structure illuminates human behavior.

A day in the life of these social monkeys includes moseying through the forest of the Tangkoko Nature Reserve, eating, grooming, and lollygagging. If individuals fan out on their own, they use calls to stay in contact with the group.

By Jennifer S. Holland
Photographs by Stefano Unterthiner

 **If it weren't for a cheeky monkey named Naruto, who, as the story goes, stole a photographer's camera in an Indonesian park and snapped a selfie, crested black macaques might still be languishing in obscurity.**

The photo later went viral, and *Macaca nigra* suddenly had millions of online fans just as the International Union for Conservation of Nature, which sets the conservation status of animals, was working toward listing the punk-haired, amber-eyed species as among the world's 25 most endangered primates.

In 2015 Naruto's selfie sparked a copyright lawsuit including the animal welfare group People for the Ethical Treatment of Animals—since the monkey took the shot, does he own it?—which could push the boundaries of animal rights. But Naruto's renown hasn't earned him special cred with his fellow macaques in the confined forests of the Tangkoko-Batuangus-Duasaudara Nature Reserve, near Bitung, on the island of Sulawesi.

"That's him," said primatologist Antje Engelhardt, of England's Liverpool John Moores University. She pointed to a beagle-size macaque sitting hunched over, scratching himself. At that moment a male named Alex approached Naruto from behind and mounted him.

"Did you see that?" Engelhardt chuckled, explaining that Alex was getting himself out of a fix. Charlie, the group's top-ranked, or alpha, male, had just grabbed a fig Alex was about to eat. "Rather than risk a fight with Charlie," Engelhardt said, "Alex turned his frustration into a show of power over a lesser animal."

So much for fame.

Under the Macaca Nigra Project, Engelhardt and a revolving cast of students have been studying the behavior and biology of the reserve's macaques for a decade. *M. nigra,* known locally as *yaki,* is one of seven distinct macaque species that evolved on Sulawesi—an Indonesian island that resembles a hastily scrawled K, with four peninsulas radiating from a mountainous center.

In recent years the critically endangered macaques have suffered as they've been hunted for their meat, taken as pets, and squeezed into ever smaller areas by illegal tree clearing for coconut plantations and villagers' garden plots. Meanwhile conservationists are fighting government plans to open wildlands to roads and industries.

Surveys from 2009 to 2010 put yaki numbers at about 2,000 in the reserve, called simply Tangkoko, and Engelhardt says their numbers have dropped since then. It's not known how many live elsewhere in North Sulawesi. A population of non-native macaques lives on Bacan Island, hundreds of miles from Sulawesi, rumored to

Even the tiniest yaki youngsters in Tangkoko have a lot of freedom to play in and explore the forest, but they don't stray far from their mothers. If hunters take a mother for meat, they may also capture her offspring for the pet trade.

Mother macaques bear one baby every 20 months or so and do most of the parenting. Wee ones nurse for less than a year but stick close for several more. Young males eventually leave to vie for position in another group.

Adult male macaques like this one weigh in at more than 20 pounds. The tree he's on may have fallen naturally, but logging, roadbuilding, and the spread of plantations have fueled the macaques' decline.

Raoul, the big alpha male of Rambo II, opened wide to show me his dagger-sharp canines, then sauntered by and swatted my calf with a stick.

have been introduced in the mid-1800s as a gift to the local sultan.

THE SCIENTISTS are studying three main yaki groups in Tangkoko. They call the most gregarious Rambo II; its members, having been studied previously and loved by tourists, were quite tame when Engelhardt arrived a decade ago. Rambo I was also studied previously, but many years ago. Engelhardt's team has rehabituated them to the wild. The third group, Pantai Batu Hitam (or Beach of the Black Rocks, for the volcanic beaches the animals visit), is the most wary of humans.

Each group has about 80 members, with a strict hierarchy. An alpha male is the preferred mate of females, but his dominance is fragile. Takeovers are often swift and bloodless, and once an alpha loses his spot, he can't get it back. Some ousted males leave the group and try to take over another. Females mostly get along, resolving spats with grooming and other peacemaking behaviors.

Where macaque territories overlap, raucous clashes can erupt. Stragglers hearing the screeches and screams of battle will rush to join in, shrieking in solidarity with those on the front line. "They can get pretty mean," Engelhardt said, referring to the skirmishes. But death in action is rare. Fights usually are quick and more theatrical than injurious, said Maura Tyrrell, a Ph.D. student from New York's University of Buffalo. That's especially true with females, "who lip-smack and nervously touch one another until males arrive. Then boom!—it's time to chase and fight." Males will herd females away from amorous competitors, but sometimes they're rough on their mates, even scarring them with

bites. "It can be brutal to watch," Tyrrell said.

Yet the macaques seem fearless in their forest home. They climb high and swing far, snapping branches as they tumble through the canopy after missed connections. Cartoonish, wide-eyed infants cling to their mothers or play together low to the ground. Cooing calls link individuals as they forage on the move, chewing on figs and other fruits, plus bugs and leaves. Facial expressions convey moods: Ritualized yawning—which starts with an oval mouth that breaks into a gaping one as the animal flings its head back—suggests tension. Scalp retraction with ears flat invites play or grooming. Chuckles, rattles, grunts, and barks—macaque talk—each have context-dependent meaning.

Tyrrell follows macaques from sunrise to sunset five days a week, studying male interactions. She's trying to learn when and how males build coalitions, which, she said, "may shed light on the same behavior in early human societies." A day's notes are routinely R-rated. "Usually tense relationships are moderated by ritualized greetings and a genital grab," she said. "Touching another's penis may be a way for males to test their relationships and negotiate future alliances." It's not about rank, she said, as grasping can be mutual. Whoever starts it, "it's a pretty vulnerable position to let another male handle your genitals."

There are other ways to make a point. During my first day in the woods, Raoul, the big alpha male of Rambo II, opened wide to show me his dagger-sharp canines, then sauntered by and swatted my calf with a stick—letting me know my place in the social order. (Low.)

With each other, the macaques rely heavily on sexual signals. "They're extreme when it comes to sexual selection," Engelhardt told me as we saw females with hyperswollen, rosy-red rear ends parade in front of potential mates. A similarly vivid scrotum on a male signifies his testosterone level and accordingly his dominance. "The redder it is, the higher his rank," she said.

The males constantly test their standing, looking to move up in the hierarchy. Higher rank means more chances to spread one's DNA via

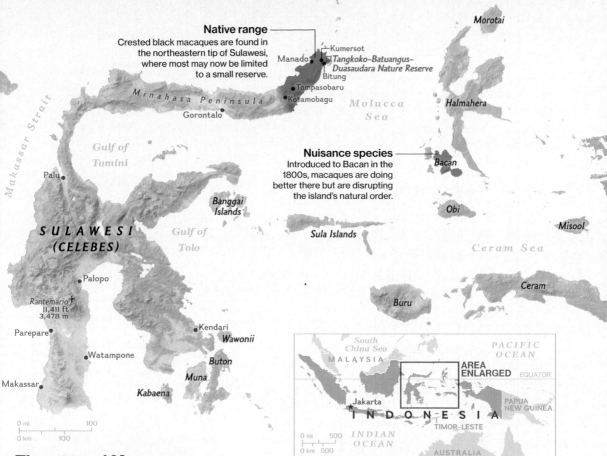

Native range
Crested black macaques are found in the northeastern tip of Sulawesi, where most may now be limited to a small reserve.

Nuisance species
Introduced to Bacan in the 1800s, macaques are doing better there but are disrupting the island's natural order.

Threatened Macaques

Crested black macaques, one of seven macaque species on Sulawesi, are considered critically endangered. Taken as pets, hunted for their meat, and faced with the illegal logging of tropical forest for agriculture—which is fragmenting their habitat—the monkeys are suffering serious decline.

fertile females (those with the biggest, reddest bottoms). "Still," Engelhardt said, "being a beta [number two] might be ideal. You don't have to be the strongest, and you still get plenty of action."

The researchers are teasing out fine details of the yaki's private life. "One exciting discovery is that males with certain personality traits—being self-confident and part of a big, diverse social network—are more likely to reach a high rank and thus sire more offspring," Engelhardt said. "So it's not your social status that affects your personality, but your personality affects your social status." The principle is true for humans too, with personality influencing social "rank" and sexual opportunities. But exactly which traits bring benefits "might be very specific," she said. "What works for male macaques might not work for men."

YAKI HAVE JUST ONE natural predator, the reticulated python, but they have many enemies. Land clearers are pushing the monkeys around.

Roadbuilders are hemming them in. And outlaw trappers have them running for their lives.

"That all used to be primary forest," Engelhardt said, nodding toward the sloping land along the main road out of Tangkoko. "First the rangers started putting in gardens, and then villagers followed suit. And up there," she pointed to the dual peaks of Mount Duasaudara, "you can see forest at the top, but the rest is [coconut] plantations now. We did surveys up there: No monkeys. Nothing."

We were driving to the Tasikoki Wildlife Rescue Centre, south of Bitung, to meet with Harry Hilser, program manager for the nonprofit Selamatkan Yaki—which works to save Sulawesi's crested black macaques—and the rescue center's manager, Simon Purser, a soft-spoken Brit who seems to carry the weight of the world on his slim frame. The center houses orphaned and injured wildlife, plus animals confiscated from smugglers and buyers of illegal "pets." Purser,

LAUREN C. TIERNEY, NGM STAFF. SOURCES: ANTJE ENGELHARDT, MACACA NIGRA PROJECT; IUCN

Stolen from the wild, young Nona (Nona means "Miss") leads a chained existence with a family in Kumersot. Keeping endangered yaki as pets is illegal; animal welfare groups are working to find and rescue them.

A butchered baby monkey laid out on scales at the market in Tompasobaru is a shocking sight to some, a promise of favored food to others. Monkeys — including yaki, their protected status ignored — are widely available in Sulawesi's Christian villages, where consumption of bush meat is common.

Raranta led me into a storage room where, from a large freezer, he pulled out the top third of a crested black macaque and propped it on a stool for my inspection.

who says he spends a lot of time "trying to get law enforcement to do their jobs," attends most raids and rescues. They can be contentious: Sometimes animals are killed rather than handed over.

Tasikoki has some 70 crested black macaques housed together in large, forested enclosures to let them establish hierarchies. "It can be a bloodbath," but that's natural, Purser said. "The goal is always to put animals back in the wild, but we can't just throw [a lone monkey] anywhere: goodbye, good luck." The risk is that the animals will get killed by territorial males "or will come out of the forest because they don't know what to do." Group releases aim to prevent such losses.

Some farmers trap macaques on purpose to keep the monkeys from raiding crops. Monkeys also get caught in traps set for pigs, birds, or rats, which can mean quick cash for a trapper. "My staff has counted [up to] a hundred traps just within a small area inside the reserve boundaries," Engelhardt said. "Unfortunately," she added, "macaques that escape traps may lose a limb to loss of circulation."

The local pet trade thrives on captured or orphaned baby macaques—often malnourished and kept in tight quarters. But the bigger threat is that people in Sulawesi have been eating macaque meat for centuries. Today it goes for about two dollars a pound (an adult macaque weighs 18 to 23 pounds), and demand spikes at holidays. The town of Tompasobaru, a six-hour drive from Tangkoko, is known for the fragrant cloves that carpet the front yards of homes, drying on tarps in the sun. But in the town's open market, the air hung heavy with the metallic smell of the butcher's wares. On sale next to dried fish and chicken

feet were rats and bats (the latter's wings in a pile like leather scraps, also for sale), plus cut-up pigs and monkeys, their faces intact.

Nofi Raranta, 37, the town's main clove dealer, is also the top hunter, employing about a hundred men who comb the surrounding forests for quarry. Raranta greeted me from the porch of his newly built house a short walk from the market, then led me into a storage room where, from a large freezer, he pulled out the top third of a crested black macaque and propped it on a stool for my inspection. He told me that his family sells about 15 macaques a week, a quarter of them yaki.

What if, I asked, you took every crested black macaque from the wild? Raranta allowed that hunters now have to go farther to find the monkeys. "I'm a businessman," he said. "We also have cloves. And there are always more rats, pigs, bats. If one animal is gone, we just look for others."

But Indonesian law protects the endangered macaques. Does he worry about getting caught with them? "Just a little. The police," Raranta said with a half smile, "they come sit and eat with us!"

"Indonesia has had an extensive legal system in place," Hilser said, "but that means nothing if it isn't enforced." And even if laws are followed, jail time for illegal hunting is rare. "Nofi might only receive a fine," Purser said. "So there's little incentive to stop what they're doing." Weak enforcement, he said, can be as bad for the species as the direct threats to their survival.

TO COUNTER the many threats, Selamatkan Yaki and the education arms of Tasikoki and the Macaca Nigra Project cooperate to try to change hearts and minds about macaques. "It's challenging to generate empathy for *M. nigra*," Purser said, "because alive they're garden pests, and dead they're food"—or cash. "First we need police working with us rather than looking away."

As for getting the support of politicians, competing interests often mean that the macaques lose out. "It's a trade-off," Akshari Masikki, an official at the Department of Conservation of Natural Resources, told me about land-use decisions. "We can't just decide things from an ecological perspective," he explained. "There

Advocates believe that teaching children to see the value of a forest full of monkeys, like this one sheltered by leaves, will bring lasting benefits and help reverse yaki's decline. "Ultimately," says longtime macaque researcher Antje Engelhardt, "we should be protecting their habitat and leaving them alone."

are economic and cultural factors to consider."

On the other hand, as fruit eaters and seed scatterers, the monkeys are "gardeners of the forest," Hilser said. "When we can make that kind of connection to the bigger picture of ecosystem function, people start to see a different kind of value—they start to get it."

Teaching kids about the macaques attracts parents' support for their protection, Hilser said. Purser adds that kids are "fantastic informants" on people who keep them as pets. In the city of Manado I met some of Selamatkan Yaki's "Yaki Ambassadors," a label of pride for annually chosen Indonesian students (and a few local notables) who speak on behalf of the macaques at schools, churches, and public events.

"What really matters is that the local communities are in," Hilser said. "That's the only way this conservation thing can work." At Tangkoko, Engelhardt has hired a former hunter, Ferdi Dalentang, to scare off the young male monkeys that tear up people's gardens in the vicinity of the reserve. "I make mad faces, yell, and chase them," he said. "Sometimes I use a slingshot on

a nearby tree to scare them. They have to take me seriously, or else they'll come right back."

A comeback is just what crested black macaques need. Hilser says ecotourism is surely part of the solution. "These monkeys are iconic. They've got great features—that punk hair and heart-shaped bum and those expressions. Yaki is a useful flagship, a mascot for Sulawesi."

As I reluctantly left Tangkoko for the last time, bumping along the trail on a motorbike, Raoul, the alpha male who had smacked my leg, wandered out from among the trees. He was alone, and after I puttered by, I glanced back to see him swagger into the middle of the path to watch me go. My guess: He was relieved that this invasive primate, one of many moving through yaki territory these days, was finally leaving—without taking anything away. □

Jennifer S. Holland is a former *National Geographic* staff writer. Her latest book is *Unlikely Friendships: Dogs.* Zoologist **Stefano Unterthiner** was a winner in the 2016 Wildlife Photographer of the Year competition, held by the Natural History Museum, in London.

Writer Mark Synnott scales a cliff in
Uzbekistan's Boysuntov Range.
Within this limestone wall lies a
winding underworld. So far, eight
missions have explored Dark Star. No
one knows how far the cave extends.

Into the Deep

Far beneath a remote mountain range in Uzbekistan, cavers delve into a labyrinth that could be the Everest of the underground.

Ice crystals populate Full Moon Hall. The chamber, 820 feet long, is the largest yet discovered in Dark Star. The entire cave system is a geological time capsule: Mineral deposits reveal millennia of climate history.

Outside the cave, it's a blistering 100°F. Inside, temperatures range from 30°F to 37°F — a small variance with a big impact on the scenery: As team members descend deeper, blue ice gives way to barren rock.

By Mark Synnott
Photographs by Robbie Shone

'Don't worry, you can't get lost down here.'

Larisa Pozdnyakova's words, in her thick Russian accent, float to me from within the cave's seemingly endless black void. Apparently, she can read my mind: All I can think about is not getting lost a mile inside the Earth. For the past several hours I've struggled to keep up as she leads me deeper into a frozen underworld known as Dark Star.

Larisa, a 30-something veteran caver from the Ural Mountains, moves with fluid, snakelike ease along our twisting route, while I grunt and heave my way after her like the clumsy rookie that I am. The cold blackness swallows the light of our headlamps just a few feet from our heads, forcing us to move like moles, scuttling, slithering, feeling our way along hundreds of feet of stiff, mud-caked ropes that help guide us through myriad passages known in caving argot as "squeezes," "meanders," and "shafts."

These passages have already been mapped, but as we crawl up and down, side to side, I feel disoriented by the nightmarish spiral of icy mud and wet gravel. For a climber and mountaineer like me, this is an altogether different kind of navigation. I'm accustomed to moving across dangerous terrain, but down here printed maps are often useless, GPS doesn't work, and there are no celestial guides to offer reassurance. And despite what Larisa tells me, I know I could never find my way out of this soul-sucking labyrinth on my own.

When I finally catch up, she has stopped at a ledge overlooking what our headlamps reveal to be a body of water—one of Dark Star's many subterranean lakes. She grabs a lanyard attached to her harness and clips it on a gritty rope attached to a bolt hammered into the rock above us. The rope leads out over the lake and disappears into the black. The setup acts as a sort of zip line to ferry cavers across the frigid lake, too cold to swim in without a wet suit. She gives me a perky smile and steps off the ledge. Her blond ponytail whips wildly in the beam of my headlamp before she vanishes into the darkness, leaving me alone with my fears.

I'M IN THIS PREDICAMENT because I signed on with a 31-member expedition—composed mostly of non-English-speaking Russians—to explore this monstrous limestone cave system inside a mountain in a remote corner of Uzbekistan. The Russians spotted an entrance to the cave in 1984, but British cavers were the first to reach it and began exploring the system in 1990; they named

A team member rappels down the face of a limestone cliff to investigate one of two large portals that could reveal a new entrance to Dark Star. Hopes were dashed; both holes led to solid ice.

How Deep Is Dark Star?

Uzbekistan's remote Boysuntov Range is hard to access, and the region is politically unstable. Still, the mysteries of Dark Star and nearby Festivalnaya—two of the world's deepest high-altitude cave systems—are an enduring lure for explorers.

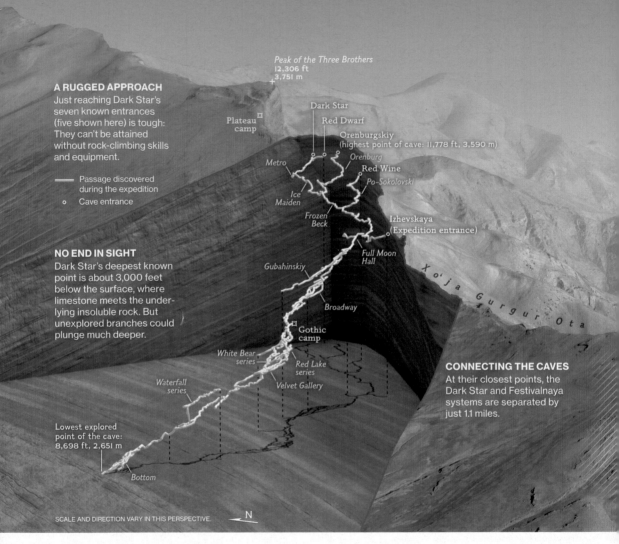

A RUGGED APPROACH
Just reaching Dark Star's seven known entrances (five shown here) is tough: They can't be attained without rock-climbing skills and equipment.

— Passage discovered during the expedition
○ Cave entrance

NO END IN SIGHT
Dark Star's deepest known point is about 3,000 feet below the surface, where limestone meets the underlying insoluble rock. But unexplored branches could plunge much deeper.

Peak of the Three Brothers
12,306 ft
3,751 m

Plateau camp

Dark Star
Red Dwarf
Orenburgskiy
(highest point of cave: 11,778 ft, 3,590 m)
Orenburg
Metro
Red Wine
Po-Sokolovski
Ice Maiden
Frozen Beck
Izhevskaya
(Expedition entrance)
Full Moon Hall
Gubahinskiy
Broadway
Gothic camp
White Bear series
Red Lake series
Velvet Gallery
Waterfall series

X o' j a   G u r g u r   O t a

CONNECTING THE CAVES
At their closest points, the Dark Star and Festivalnaya systems are separated by just 1.1 miles.

Lowest explored point of the cave:
8,698 ft, 2,651 m

Bottom

SCALE AND DIRECTION VARY IN THIS PERSPECTIVE.   N

it after a satirical American sci-fi movie from the 1970s. In the decades since, Dark Star, along with neighboring Festivalnaya (the two systems may someday be found to be connected), has drawn hard-core cavers from around the world.

The allure of this huge system is similar to that which big mountains hold for climbers—with one

difference: We know that Mount Everest is Earth's highest peak, but the potential for conquering new and enormous subterranean voids is almost limitless. More is known about the terrain of Mars than about what lies hidden beneath the Earth's surface. Krubera Cave in the republic of Georgia is currently the deepest known cave, at 7,208 feet. But Dark Star, with so many areas still to survey, is a prime candidate to take over the title.

To date, eight expeditions have identified nearly

■ **Society Grant** Your National Geographic Society membership helped fund this expedition.

CHARLES PREPPERNAU, NGM STAFF. SOURCES: ANTONINA (TONYA) VOTINTSEVA AND ZHENYA TSURIKHIN, EKATERINBURG SPELEOLOGICAL CLUB; PAZ VALE, ELDON POTHOLE CLUB. SATELLITE IMAGE: DIGITALGLOBE

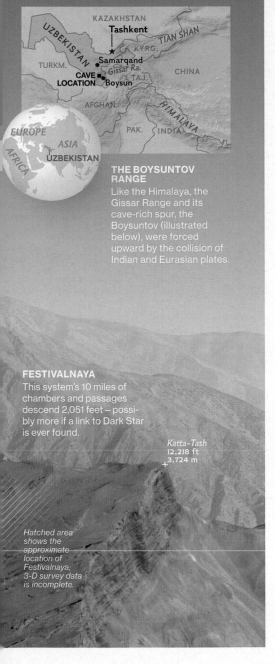

THE BOYSUNTOV
RANGE
Like the Himalaya, the
Gissar Range and its
cave-rich spur, the
Boysuntov (illustrated
below), were forced
upward by the collision of
Indian and Eurasian plates.

FESTIVALNAYA
This system's 10 miles of
chambers and passages
descend 2,051 feet — possibly more if a link to Dark Star
is ever found.

Katta-Tash
12,218 ft
3,724 m

Hatched area
shows the
approximate
location of
Festivalnaya;
3-D survey data
is incomplete.

11 miles of Dark Star's passageways, the deepest lying about 3,000 feet below the surface. But the system hasn't been fully mapped, partly because of
its remote location in a politically unstable region
and partly because its vastness requires advanced
technical abilities and a lot of equipment. Many
expeditions have simply run out of rope. I can im-
mediately see why. Just a thousand feet from our
entry point, Larisa and I had already negotiated
nearly a dozen roped sections.

She and I had been paired at base camp: her
assignment, to guide the "Amerikanski" (I'm sure
I heard them calling me that) to Gothic camp,
more than a mile inside the mountain. I would
spend two nights recording the team's progress
in mapping new parts of the cave and collecting
scientific data.

NEVER MIND THE PERILOUS TRIP following
Larisa to Gothic camp—the aboveground journey to our base camp at the foot of the mountain
was no walk in the park either. To meet up with
the expedition team—an ensemble of world-class
cavers and scientists ages 22 to 54 that, in addition
to the Russians, included Italians, Israelis, and
one German—I traveled to Tashkent, the capital
of Uzbekistan. From there we traveled together a
little over a hundred miles by bus, with hundreds
of pounds of food and gear for three weeks in the
field, across the arid plains. We took a popular
tourist route that follows the ancient Silk Road
to Samarqand. Then we turned off the beaten
path, heading south toward the Afghan border
to Boysun, where we loaded everything into a six-
wheeled Soviet-era troop transport.

As we lumbered into the Boysuntov (also
known as Baysun-Tau) Range, the mountains
gradually rose to 12,000 feet and then dropped
off in a jagged line of spectacular cliffs. In the deep
valleys between we could see a hodgepodge of
small villages where Tajiks and Uzbeks have lived
for centuries, herding goats and harvesting water-
melons, plums, apples, and walnuts and fetching
water from springs fed by the underground rivers
that perforate these mountains.

It was some 30 years ago that Igor Lavrov, the
heavily bearded, bespectacled geologist who now
sat across from me in the back of the truck, discovered the towering limestone cliff called Xo'ja
Gurgur Ota that he and his fellow cavers are still
exploring all these years later. This wall, 1,200 feet
high and 22 miles long, was formed when tectonic
forces thrust ancient beds of limestone into ver-
tical walls of rock. Igor was a 24-year-old junior
member of the Sverdlovsk Speleological Club,
which had learned about the Boysuntov by studying old Soviet geologic maps. One day, following a

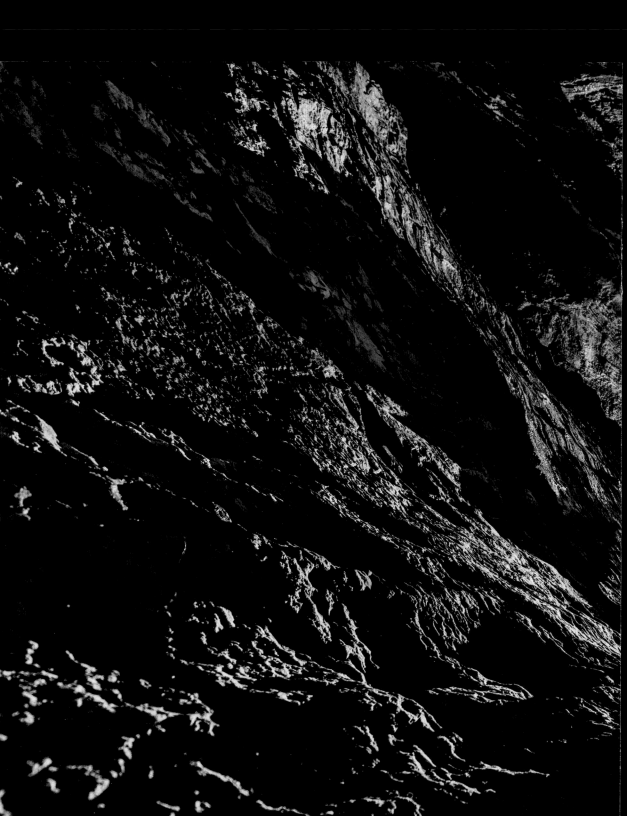

Zhenya Tsurikhin climbs a free-hanging rope. Dark Star's passages are deep underground, yet many are 10,000 feet above sea level. The thin air at that altitude ups the physical challenge of negotiating the cave

tip from an itinerant shepherd, he and a companion, Sergei Matrenin, met the schoolmaster of a small village named Qayroq. The man had spent years exploring nearby grottoes with homemade torches. "Where can I find these caves?" asked Igor. "There," said the schoolmaster, pointing to the monolithic limestone wall at the head of the valley. From the bottom of the rock face, the two cavers first spotted the mysterious hole halfway up the cliff that was to be our entrance to Dark Star.

Once the route became too steep for the truck, we hiked for two days with 15 donkeys to haul our supplies up to the base camp, perched on sloping terraces at the foot of the limestone escarpment. All of Dark Star's seven known entrances are found on this face and can only be reached via technical climbing or rappelling.

It took us several days of rigging ropes to access the cave and haul up gear. But finally I hoisted myself up a 450-foot rope to the cave's main entrance (dubbed Izhevskaya, or R21). I began to see why cavers think of Dark Star as a living, breathing entity. Down at base camp, the temperature hovered around 100°F, but up here I was shocked to find myself bracing against a freezing wind blasting out of Dark Star's mouth.

No one fully understands the cave's ventilation system, but this particular entrance "exhales" when the barometric pressure outside is high and "inhales" when the pressure is low. If Dark Star was exhaling here, it must have been sucking in air somewhere else. But where? As I scurried down a frost-covered slope into the cave, I couldn't shake the distinct feeling that I was stepping into the maw of a prehistoric beast.

Just inside the entrance, Tonya Votintseva, a Russian molecular biologist, stopped to attach a small white disk to the wall. Her official assignment is to map any newly discovered areas of the cave, but she admits she is more interested in science than exploration. This data logger is one of several she will install throughout the cave to record the temperature, humidity, carbon dioxide level, and barometric pressure for the next two years. Then they'll be collected and taken to a lab for analysis.

A lot of science can be gathered underground, much of it contained in speleothems—mineral deposits called stalagmites and stalactites that rise from cave floors and descend from the ceilings. In the same way that scientists use ice core samples taken from glaciers, they can gather data from speleothems. By analyzing the chemical components delivered to these formations by drip water over millennia, they can get clues to Earth's climate at various points in time.

Each year the team collects samples from different parts of the cave system to gain insight into not only the climate history of Central Asia but also the cave's ventilation system and architecture—knowledge that helps future cavers determine where to find promising new passages to explore. Following Tonya, I duck under an archway of translucent blue ice and enter a massive chamber some 820 feet long and a hundred feet tall—the Full Moon Hall. Turning my headlamp to its full brightness, I pan across the room. The walls are covered with delicate feathers of hoarfrost that blink in the light like millions of tiny mirrors, illuminating the hall like galaxies of stars in a crystal clear night sky.

TWO DAYS LATER I am at the edge of a lake with Larisa, who's out of sight, waiting for me on the other side. At least I hope she is. Since I joined the team, the Russians have seemed intent on reminding me of my rookie status, telling campfire stories of cavers who met with tragic ends, including a young explorer who made a wrong turn and got lost in a cave in Britain. "One year later they found his body," one of them tells me. They've also been poking me with random challenges that seem designed to determine whether the Amerikanski can hang with them—seeing how heavy a load I can carry, how good my rope skills are, how much I'll let them screw with me.

There's only one thing to do. I clip my harness to the rope and slide to the other side of the lake, touching down on a ledge that leads into a small domed chamber roughly the size of a large igloo.

Perched on slippery rock, Synnott knows that falling into icy water isn't an option. Here, wet clothes won't dry. Hypothermia, a broken ankle, or getting lost are just a few of the risks that loom in Dark Star.

Larisa is not there. The current challenge seems to be to see whether I can find my way alone. So far, I've met their tests with competence and a good-natured laugh. But I'm not laughing now. A quick pan with my headlamp reveals two passages that spoke off from the chamber. I strain to hear any noise that might reveal which one Larisa has disappeared into, but all I can hear is the sound of water dripping from the ceiling into the lake.

As I contemplate my options, I turn off my light to conserve the batteries. The blackness that envelops me is absolute. Photons of light travel billions of miles through the universe in straight, unobstructed lines, but they cannot bend. The twisting path that leads deep into the mountain restricts the only light that will ever shine on these walls to the beams of headlamps. I think about how the lost British caver must have felt as his lamp died, lying alone in what would become his tomb.

"LARISA!" I yell, but the sound just bounces off the walls in the tiny chamber. It suddenly becomes clear: Her "don't worry, you can't get lost" thing is some kind of insiders' joke, because actually you can, quite easily.

The first passageway I follow turns quickly, mercifully, into a dead end. The second one leads me to a ledge of glossy flowstone formed by thin sheets of minerals deposited by a consistent flow of water. Larisa is sitting on it.

On we go to a T-shaped intersection where two

brightly colored tents, glowing with light, sit atop a pile of jumbled boulders: Gothic camp. A headlamp beam bobs in our direction and the voice of Zhenya Tsurikhin booms: "Welcome to Gothic Chamber." Zhenya is the group's elder statesman, on his 10th caving expedition to the Boysuntov. He breeds fish for a Russian state institute, but Dark Star is his true life's work, and no one understands the cave's complex networks better than he does. "He knows where new passages will lead before they are explored," one of the younger Russians tells me.

Zhenya gestures toward one of the tents. Steam pours from its opening, and I can hear a stove purring inside. I slip out of my coveralls and follow him into the tent, where a few team members are huddled around a map of Dark Star. Passages discovered during each expedition are rendered in different colors, and the map looks like a multicolored schematic of the human circulatory system. Tracing a sinuous green line with a muddy finger, Zhenya taps a spot and begins speaking rapidly in Russian. He's pointing to where the previous expedition ran into an impasse at a 120-foot waterfall. It has yet to be climbed.

I spend my first night deep in the bowels of the Earth, jammed into a tent with two other team members. Down here, day and night are irrelevant, and the team comes and goes, sleeps and eats, on a schedule unhindered by the position of the sun. I awake to the loud arrival of three Israeli cavers who have spent four days worming through a rubble-filled crack at the bottom of the cave. One of them is Boaz Langford, a young geologist who tells me he thinks they've reached the nonporous rock underlying the limestone. "We need to find a new direction," he says. "We are going to explore the Red Lakes. You should come with us."

Instead of waiting for me to suit up, he rattles off some quick instructions and is gone. Half an hour later, I am alone in the dark again, facing another fork in the road. There are two ropes: One drops straight down through a slot in the floor; the other angles upward and traverses an abyss—a deep pit or possibly a lake, I can't tell—and disappears into a hole 20 feet above me. I opt for the slot in the floor and descend between overhanging walls of rippled orange flowstone to find another intersection of three passages with no indication of which way the Israelis might have gone.

I pick the least worst option: a tube about the size of an air duct filled with four inches of water. I shove my backpack in and nudge it forward with my head. I hold my torso out of the water by perching on my forearms and toes, inching forward in a gut-crushing plank position. The ceiling lowers until I'm forced to slither on my belly. Suddenly the tube turns almost straight down. It's so tight that just flexing my muscles keeps me from diving down the shaft.

As the blood rushes to my head, another caving horror story comes to mind. A young American medical student was exploring a virgin passage in Utah's Nutty Putty Cave in 2009 when it suddenly took a downward turn. He dropped in headfirst, assuming it would eventually open up. Instead it got tighter, and he ended up trapped upside down. Rescuers found him and were even able to get food and water to him as they worked. They almost got him out, but their equipment failed. They weren't able to extract his dead body, so the passage was filled with concrete.

I am more fortunate, and when the tube spits me out into a water-filled corridor, I hear the sound of cave suits scraping against rock. I've found the Israelis. And they have found another small hole

that drops even farther into the unknown depths of Dark Star. They are arguing over who gets to go in first. "It's mine," one says in Hebrew as he shoves his friends aside and dives into the hole.

AS TIME RUNS OUT on the expedition, most of the hoped-for new passages have proved to be dead ends. The team has exited the cave and is preparing for the long journey back to Tashkent, but Zhenya, along with an ambitious young Russian named Aleksey Seregin, insists on making one more push to climb the big waterfall and find a new passage.

When they finally return to the base camp, where we're still waiting for them three days later, they are coated with grime and brimming with the news that they climbed the waterfall and after hours of shimmying in tight meander, it pinched down to a slot, barely nine inches wide. Aleksey tried to enter the fissure, but his head simply wouldn't fit. Refusing to give up, Zhenya tried, jamming his head into the crack, his temples scraping against the icy rock. Tilting his shoulders and sucking in his belly, he wormed up a twisting chimney. After 30 minutes of contorting himself to move inch after painstaking inch, he finally popped through the crack into a passageway as big as a Moscow subway tunnel and reverberating with the roar of a fast-flowing river.

Was this the passage that he'd been seeking for more than 20 years? The one that will finally reveal Dark Star to be the Everest of caves? He desperately wanted to keep going, to see where it would lead. But alas, the expedition's time had run out.

As the men relate their story, the jolt of the new discovery pulses through the team, and it becomes clear, even to the Amerikanski, that this is exactly how great caving expeditions should end: with the discovery of a mysterious passage snaking into the unknown—and the promise of a new adventure waiting deep inside the Earth. □

Mark Synnott's search for unclimbed rock walls has taken him on some 30 expeditions around the world. He wrote about the Aral Sea for a June 2015 feature in *National Geographic*. **Robbie Shone** is based in Innsbruck, Austria. This is his first story for the magazine.

METROPOLIS

With more than half the world's population
concentrated in urban areas, megacities are
a swirl of 21st-century energy and humanity.

A bus stop, a digital photo lab, and traditional vendors share space on a corner in Karachi, Pakistan.

Story and Photographs
by Martin Roemers

More people live in cities than ever before. According to the United Nations Population Fund, over half of the world's citizens now live in an urban area—a figure expected to reach nearly 70 percent by 2050. Globally, one in eight of those city dwellers lives in a megacity, defined by the UN as a place with more than 10 million people.

That's why I started this series, which I call "Metropolis." I wanted to focus on the UN statistics—and show what they actually look like. So from 2007 to 2015 I photographed megacities and documented the dynamic process of urbanization.

I asked myself several questions: How can people live in cities that are so crowded, hectic, and chaotic? What are the differences among these megacities? And what do they have in common?

I try to expose the contrasts between wealth and poverty, traditional culture and cutting-edge development. I'm fascinated that so many people can coexist in such crowded places. There's never enough space. But there's also a current of inventiveness, a sense of community.

Whenever I work in a new city, I enlist a local assistant. We discuss which locations we should visit, and if a spot looks good, we find a high vantage point. Then it becomes a waiting game.

To visualize the speed of urban life and capture its energy, I use long exposure times. It's important to know which elements in the frame are moving and which are still. There has to be a balance—a harmony in the chaos.

All my photos are shot on film. My aim is to encapsulate megacity life in a single photograph—one panoramic, kaleidoscopic image. All the photos in this series are multilayered: The longer you look, especially at large prints, the more you see. I've pored over these pictures a thousand times, but I still manage to find new stories and elements each time. I hope you will too. ☐

AS TOLD TO JEREMY BERLIN

This shot of the Eiffel Tower was taken from a park. When I first set up there, the police asked if I had a permit. It took my agent three weeks to get the right one. Shooting in some Western cities can be difficult because of bureaucracy. But it's worth it.

Tokyo's Shibuya Crossing may be the busiest intersection in the world. Usually I use a two-to-four-second exposure, but this one is eight or 10, which makes the image abstract. You can see a sea of people here, but you can't recognize most of them as individuals — just the ones who are standing still.

Seen from a rooftop, the urban bustle of Lagos, Nigeria, is a blurry mosaic of colors. Africa is a rapidly urbanizing continent. By 2030 its three current megacities — Lagos, Cairo, and Kinshasa — will likely be joined by Dar es Salaam, Johannesburg, and Luanda.

I want each image to be a story. Kolkata, India, is a city known for its hand-pulled rickshaws. I knew I wanted one in this photo, but rickshaw drivers never stop unless there's a streetcar. Fortunately, this tram on Lenin Sarani Road comes every few minutes, so I knew I was in the right spot.

Martin Roemers's book on megacities, *Metropolis,* was published in 2015. This series has been exhibited in cities worldwide. Works from "Metropolis" are included in the Rijksmuseum in Amsterdam and the Museum of Fine Arts in Houston, Texas.

DRY AS DEATH

By Patricia Edmonds

In the high plains of Bolivia, a man surveys the baked remains of what was the country's second largest lake. For centuries locals rafted on the waters and lived off the fish and waterfowl of Lake Poopó. Once covering some 1,100 square miles, the lake had shrunk and resurged in the past—but in late 2015 it virtually vanished. In a coming issue Kenneth R. Weiss will report on its demise.

Some three-fourths of jobs in the global workforce are dependent on water, according to a 2016 UN report on water and development. Agriculture, fishing, energy, transport—if their water sources dry up, livelihoods do too.

Many lakes face a common menace: climate change. When its effects alter habitats, disrupt food webs, and spawn extreme weather, that can lead to people being "uprooted from their homes," Weiss says. War drives much of today's forced migration, but climate change also is a factor, he says.

What doomed Lake Poopó? Water diversions upstream, weather extremes—and perhaps, one man told Weiss, too few sacrifices to the rain gods. But other locals—those who haven't left—don't dwell much on causes, Weiss says, "they're just trying to figure out how the hell they're going to feed their kids tonight."

To go **FURTHER** into this topic, watch the documentary *Water & Power: A California Heist* at 9 ET/PT on March 14, and the three-part miniseries *Parched* at 9 ET/PT on March 21, March 28, and April 4 on National Geographic.